# It's another great book from CGP...

If you're taking the **AQA Level 2 Certificate in Further Maths**, this book explains everything you'll need to know for the exams.

It's packed with clear study notes and worked examples for every topic, plus brain-teasing practice questions to test you on what you've learned.

It even includes a **free** Online Edition you can read on your computer or tablet!

## How to get your free Online Edition

Just go to **cgpbooks.co.uk/extras** and enter this code...

3754 6740 1641 0814

By the way, this code only works for one person. If somebody else has used this book before you, they might have already claimed the Online Edition.

# CGP — still the best! ☺

Our sole aim here at CGP is to produce the highest quality books — carefully written, immaculately presented and dangerously close to being funny.

Then we work our socks off to get them out to you
— at the cheapest possible prices.

Published by CGP

Written by Richard Parsons

Editors: Kirstie McHale, Sarah Oxley, David Ryan and Caley Simpson

With thanks to Jane Appleton and Simon Little for the proofreading

ISBN: 978 1 78294 179 8

Printed by Elanders Ltd, Newcastle upon Tyne.
Clipart from Corel®

0800 1712 712  •  www.cgpbooks.co.uk

# Contents

# Fractions

Here's a nice gentle reminder on how to deal with <u>fractions</u> (without a calculator) to ease you into this book.

## 1) Cancelling down — easy

To <u>cancel down</u> or <u>simplify</u> a fraction, <u>divide top and bottom by the same number</u>, till they won't go further:

**EXAMPLE:**  Simplify $\frac{18}{24}$.

Cancel down in a series of <u>easy steps</u> — keep going till the top and bottom don't have <u>any</u> common factors.

$$\overset{\div 3 \quad\quad \div 2}{\frac{18}{24} = \frac{6}{8} = \frac{3}{4}}_{\div 3 \quad\quad \div 2}$$

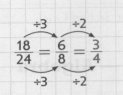

The number on the top of the fraction is the <u>numerator</u>, and the number on the bottom is the <u>denominator</u>.

## 2) Mixed numbers — quite easy

<u>Mixed numbers</u> are things like $3\frac{1}{3}$, with an integer part and a fraction part. <u>Improper fractions</u> are ones where the top number is larger than the bottom number. You need to be able to convert between the two.

**EXAMPLES:**

**1.** Write $4\frac{2}{3}$ as an improper fraction.

1) Think of the <u>mixed number</u> as an <u>addition</u>:
$$4\frac{2}{3} = 4 + \frac{2}{3}$$

2) Turn the <u>integer part</u> into a <u>fraction</u>:
$$4 + \frac{2}{3} = \frac{12}{3} + \frac{2}{3} = \frac{12+2}{3} = \frac{14}{3}$$

**2.** Write $\frac{31}{4}$ as a mixed number.

<u>Divide</u> the top number by the bottom.

1) The <u>answer</u> gives the <u>whole number part</u>.

2) The <u>remainder</u> goes <u>on top</u> of the fraction.

$$31 \div 4 = 7 \text{ remainder } 3 \quad \text{so} \quad \frac{31}{4} = 7\frac{3}{4}$$

## 3) Multiplying — easy

Multiply top and bottom separately. It usually helps to cancel down first if you can.

**EXAMPLE:**  Find $\frac{8}{15} \times \frac{5}{12}$.

<u>Cancel down</u> by dividing top and bottom by any common factors you find in <u>either</u> fraction:

Now multiply the top and bottom numbers <u>separately</u>:

8 and 12 both divide by 4

15 and 5 both divide by 5

$$\frac{^2\cancel{8}}{15} \times \frac{5}{_3\cancel{12}} = \frac{2}{\cancel{15}_3} \times \frac{^1\cancel{5}}{3}$$
$$= \frac{2}{3} \times \frac{1}{3} = \frac{2 \times 1}{3 \times 3} = \frac{2}{9}$$

## 4) Dividing — quite easy

Turn the 2nd fraction <u>UPSIDE DOWN</u> and then <u>multiply</u>:

**EXAMPLE:**  Find $2\frac{1}{3} \div 3\frac{1}{2}$.

Rewrite the <u>mixed numbers</u> as <u>fractions</u>:  $2\frac{1}{3} \div 3\frac{1}{2} = \frac{7}{3} \div \frac{7}{2}$

Turn $\frac{7}{2}$ <u>upside down</u> and <u>multiply</u>:  $= \frac{7}{3} \times \frac{2}{7}$

<u>Simplify</u> by cancelling the 7s:  $= \frac{1}{3} \times \frac{2}{1} = \frac{2}{3}$

When you're multiplying or dividing with mixed numbers, <u>always</u> turn them into improper fractions first.

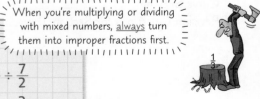

# Fractions

## 5) Common denominators — slightly trickier

This comes in handy for <u>ordering fractions</u> by size, and for <u>adding</u> or <u>subtracting</u> fractions.
You need to find a number that <u>all</u> the denominators <u>divide into</u> — this will be your <u>common denominator</u>.
The simplest way is to find the <u>lowest common multiple</u> of the denominators:

**EXAMPLE:** Put these fractions in ascending order of size: $\dfrac{8}{3}, \dfrac{5}{4}, \dfrac{12}{5}$

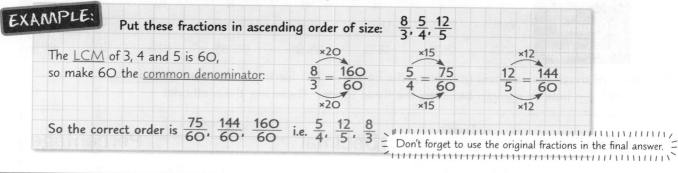

The <u>LCM</u> of 3, 4 and 5 is 60,
so make 60 the <u>common denominator</u>:

$$\frac{8}{3} = \frac{160}{60} \quad (\times 20)$$

$$\frac{5}{4} = \frac{75}{60} \quad (\times 15)$$

$$\frac{12}{5} = \frac{144}{60} \quad (\times 12)$$

So the correct order is $\dfrac{75}{60}, \dfrac{144}{60}, \dfrac{160}{60}$ i.e. $\dfrac{5}{4}, \dfrac{12}{5}, \dfrac{8}{3}$

*Don't forget to use the original fractions in the final answer.*

## 6) Adding, subtracting — sort the denominators first

1) Make sure the denominators are <u>the same</u> (see above).
2) Add (or subtract) the top lines (numerators) <u>only</u>.

If you're adding or subtracting <u>mixed numbers</u>, it usually helps to convert them to improper fractions first.

**EXAMPLE:** Calculate $2\frac{1}{5} - 1\frac{1}{2}$.

Rewrite the <u>mixed numbers</u> as <u>fractions</u>:

$$2\frac{1}{5} - 1\frac{1}{2} = \frac{11}{5} - \frac{3}{2}$$

Find a <u>common denominator</u>:

$$= \frac{22}{10} - \frac{15}{10}$$

Combine the <u>top lines</u>:

$$= \frac{22 - 15}{10} = \frac{7}{10}$$

*People usually find adding and subtracting fractions harder than multiplying and dividing — but it's actually pretty easy as long as you remember to make sure the denominators are the same.*

## 7) Finding a fraction of something — just multiply

<u>Multiply</u> the 'something' by the <u>TOP</u> of the fraction, and <u>divide</u> it by the <u>BOTTOM</u>.
It doesn't matter which order you do those two steps in — just start with whatever's easiest.

**EXAMPLE:** What is $\dfrac{9}{20}$ of £360?

Start by dividing by 20, that's easiest:

$$\frac{9}{20} \text{ of } £360 = (£360 \div 20) \times 9$$
$$= £18 \times 9$$
$$= £162$$

## No fractions were harmed in the making of these pages...

...although one was slightly frightened for a while, and several were tickled.
When you think you've learnt all this, try all of these questions without a calculator.

Q1  Calculate:  a) $\dfrac{3}{10} \times 1\dfrac{5}{8}$  [3 marks]    b) $1\dfrac{7}{12} \div 2\dfrac{3}{8}$  [3 marks]

c) $3\dfrac{5}{12} + 2\dfrac{9}{24}$  [3 marks]    d) $2\dfrac{3}{4} - 4\dfrac{5}{6}$  [3 marks]

Q2  Caroline has made 560 sandwiches. $\dfrac{2}{7}$ of the sandwiches are tuna, $\dfrac{5}{8}$ are cheese

and the rest are ham. How many ham sandwiches has Caroline made?  [4 marks]

# Fractions, Decimals and Percentages

Here's a quick recap on the three different types of <u>PROPORTION</u>. Fractions, decimals and percentages are <u>three different ways</u> of expressing a <u>proportion</u> of something — they're <u>closely related and completely interchangeable</u> with each other. This table shows the really common conversions which you should know straight off without having to work them out:

| Fraction | $\frac{1}{2}$ | $\frac{1}{4}$ | $\frac{3}{4}$ | $\frac{1}{3}$ | $\frac{2}{3}$ | $\frac{1}{10}$ | $\frac{1}{5}$ | $\frac{2}{5}$ |
|---|---|---|---|---|---|---|---|---|
| Decimal | 0.5 | 0.25 | 0.75 | 0.3333... | 0.6666... | 0.1 | 0.2 | 0.4 |
| Percentage | 50% | 25% | 75% | $33.\dot{3}\%$ | $66.\dot{6}\%$ | 10% | 20% | 40% |

The more of those conversions you learn, the better — but for those that you <u>don't know</u>, you must <u>learn</u> how to <u>convert</u> between the three types. These are the methods:

$$\text{Fraction} \xrightarrow{\text{Divide}} \text{Decimal} \xrightarrow{\times \text{ by 100}} \text{Percentage}$$

E.g. $\frac{7}{20}$ is $7 \div 20$ = 0.35     e.g. $0.35 \times 100$ = 35%

$$\text{Fraction} \xleftarrow[\text{The awkward one}]{} \text{Decimal} \xleftarrow[\div \text{ by 100}]{} \text{Percentage}$$

<u>Converting decimals to fractions</u> is awkward, because it's different for different types of decimal. There are two different methods you need to learn:

1) <u>Terminating decimals</u> to fractions — this is fairly easy. The digits after the decimal point go on the top, and a <u>power of 10</u> on the bottom — with the same number of zeros as there were decimal places.

e.g. $0.6 = \frac{6}{10}$, $0.12 = \frac{12}{100}$, $0.05 = \frac{5}{100}$, $0.345 = \frac{345}{1000}$, $0.024 = \frac{24}{1000}$ etc.

2) <u>Recurring decimals</u> to fractions — this is trickier. See below...

## Recurring or Terminating...

1) <u>Recurring</u> decimals have a <u>pattern</u> of numbers which repeats forever, e.g. $\frac{1}{3}$ is the decimal 0.333333... Note, it doesn't have to be a single digit that repeats. You could have, for instance: 0.143143143....

2) The <u>repeating part</u> is usually marked with <u>dots</u> or a <u>bar</u> on top of the number. If there's one dot, then only one digit is repeated. If there are two dots, then everything from the first dot to the second dot is the repeating bit. E.g. $0.2\dot{5} = 0.2555555...$, $0.\dot{2}\dot{5} = 0.25252525...$, $0.\dot{2}5\dot{5} = 0.255255255...$

3) <u>Terminating</u> decimals are <u>finite</u> (they come to an end), e.g $\frac{1}{20}$ is the decimal 0.05.

## Recurring Decimals into Fractions

This is something you probably won't have to do all that often (if at all), so you can make do with using the '<u>Just Learning the Result</u>' method:

1) The fraction always has the <u>repeating unit</u> on the top and <u>the same number of nines</u> on the bottom...

e.g. $0.206206206206... = 0.\dot{2}0\dot{6} = \frac{206}{999}$

2) <u>BUT</u> this <u>only</u> works if the repeating bit starts <u>straight after</u> the decimal point.

## Eight out of ten cats prefer the perfume Eighty Purr Scent...

Learn the whole of the top table and the 4 conversion processes. Then it's time to break into a mild sweat...

Q1    Turn the following decimals into fractions in their simplest form.
a) 0.8    b) 0.04    c) 0.55    d) 0.777    e) 6.4     [5 marks]

Q2    Which is greater:    a) 45% or $\frac{5}{11}$    b) $\frac{5}{8}$ or 63%?    [2 marks]

Q3    Write $0.0\dot{7}\dot{2}$ as a fraction in its simplest form.     [2 marks]

# Percentages

I'll whizz through the different types of questions on <u>percentages</u> that you might come across. You've probably seen them all before, so this will be a walk in the park.

## *Three Simple Question Types*

### Type 1 — "Find x% of y"

Turn the percentage into a <u>decimal</u>, then <u>multiply</u>.

**EXAMPLE:**  Find 15% of £46.
1) Write 15% as a <u>decimal</u>:      15% = 15 ÷ 100 = 0.15
2) <u>Multiply</u> £46 by 0.15:     0.15 × £46 = £6.90

### Type 2 — "Find the new amount after a % increase/decrease"

Turn the percentage into a <u>decimal</u>, then <u>multiply</u>. Add this on (or subtract from) the original value.

**EXAMPLE:**  A toaster is reduced in price by 40% in the sales. It originally cost £68. What is the new price of the toaster?
1) Write 40% as a <u>decimal</u>:     40% = 40 ÷ 100 = 0.4
2) <u>Multiply</u> to find 40% <u>of</u> £68:     0.4 × £68 = £27.20
3) It's a decrease, so subtract from the original:     £68 − £27.20 = £40.80

> You should also know how to use the <u>multiplier</u> method:
> multiplier = 1 − 0.4
> = 0.6
> **68 × 0.6 = £40.80**

### Type 3 — "Express x as a percentage of y"

<u>Divide</u> x by y, then multiply by <u>100</u>.

**EXAMPLE:**  Give 40p as a percentage of £3.34.
1) Make sure both amounts are in the <u>same units</u> — convert £3.34 to pence:     £3.34 = 334p
2) <u>Divide</u> 40p by 334p, <u>then multiply</u> by 100:     (40 ÷ 334) × 100 = 12.0% (1 d.p.)

## *A Trickier Question Type*

1) This is the formula for giving a <u>change in value</u> as a <u>percentage</u> — **LEARN IT, AND USE IT:**

$$\text{PERCENTAGE 'CHANGE'} = \frac{\text{'CHANGE'}}{\text{ORIGINAL}} \times 100$$

2) This is similar to Type 3 above, because you end up with a <u>percentage</u> rather than an amount.
3) Typical questions will ask 'Find the percentage <u>increase</u>/<u>profit</u>/<u>error</u>' or 'Calculate the percentage <u>decrease</u>/<u>loss</u>/<u>discount</u>', etc.

---

## *Fact: 70% of people understand percentages, the other 40% don't...*

Learn the details for each type of percentage question, then turn over and write it all down.
Then try these questions:

Q1    Increase 650 by 24%.                 [2 marks]

Q2    Frank bought an ostrich for £5600. He later sold it for £3696.
      Calculate Frank's percentage loss.             [3 marks]

Q3    A car is reduced in price by 15% to £12 410. What did it cost before?     [3 marks]

# Ratios

<u>Ratios</u> can pop up in all sorts of different questions — here's a reminder of the basic ratio skills you need to tackle any ratio question that might come your way.

## *Reducing Ratios to their Simplest Form*

To reduce a ratio to a <u>simpler form</u>, divide <u>all the numbers</u> in the ratio by the <u>same thing</u> (a bit like simplifying a fraction). It's in its <u>simplest form</u> when there's nothing left you can divide by.

**EXAMPLE:** Write the ratio 15:18 in its simplest form.

For the ratio 15:18, both numbers have a <u>factor</u> of 3, so <u>divide them by 3</u>.

We can't reduce this any further. So the simplest form of 15:18 is 5:6.

$$÷3 \left( \begin{array}{c} 15:18 \\ \downarrow \\ 5:6 \end{array} \right) ÷3$$

---

**A handy trick for the calculator paper — use the fraction button**

If you enter a fraction with the ▢ or $a^b_c$ button, the calculator automatically cancels it down when you press ▭ .

So for the ratio 8:12, just enter $\frac{8}{12}$ as a fraction, and you'll get the reduced fraction $\frac{2}{3}$.

Now you just change it back to ratio form, i.e. <u>2 : 3</u>. Ace.

## *The More Awkward Cases:*

### *1) If the ratio contains decimals or fractions — multiply*

**EXAMPLES:**

**1.** Simplify the ratio 2.4:3.6 as far as possible.

1) <u>Multiply both sides by 10</u> to get rid of the decimal parts.
2) Now <u>divide</u> to reduce the ratio to its simplest form.

$$\begin{array}{l} ×10 \left( \begin{array}{c} 2.4:3.6 \\ \downarrow \\ 24:36 \end{array} \right) ×10 \\ ÷12 \left( \begin{array}{c} \\ \downarrow \\ 2:3 \end{array} \right) ÷12 \end{array}$$

**2.** Give the ratio $\frac{5}{4} : \frac{7}{2}$ in its simplest form.

1) Put the fractions over a <u>common denominator</u> (see p3).
2) Multiply <u>both sides</u> by 4 to get rid of the fractions.
3) This ratio won't cancel further, so we're done.

$$\frac{5}{4} : \frac{7}{2}$$
$$×4 \left( \frac{5}{4} : \frac{14}{4} \right) ×4$$
$$5:14$$

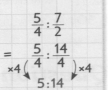

I ain't gettin' on no gosh-darned plane!

Don't be so awkward, case.

### *2) If the ratio has mixed units — convert to the smaller unit*

**EXAMPLE:** Reduce the ratio 24 mm : 7.2 cm to its simplest form.

1) <u>Convert</u> 7.2 cm to millimetres.
2) <u>Simplify</u> the resulting ratio. Once the units on both sides are the same, <u>get rid of them</u> for the final answer.

$$\begin{array}{l} 24 \text{ mm}:7.2 \text{ cm} \\ = 24 \text{ mm}:72 \text{ mm} \\ ÷24 \searrow 1:3 \swarrow ÷24 \end{array}$$

### *3) To get the form 1 : n or n : 1 — just divide*

**EXAMPLE:** Reduce 3:56 to the form 1:n.

Divide both sides by 3:

$$÷3 \left( \begin{array}{c} 3:56 \\ \downarrow \\ 1: \frac{56}{3} \end{array} \right) ÷3 = 1:18\frac{2}{3} \text{ (or } 1:18.\dot{6})$$

This form is often the <u>most useful</u>, since it shows the ratio very clearly.

# Ratios

There's just so much <u>great stuff</u> to say about ratios. I couldn't possibly fit it onto only one page...

## Scaling Up Ratios

If you know the <u>ratio between parts</u> and the actual size of <u>one part</u>, you can <u>scale the ratio up</u> to find the other parts.

 **EXAMPLE:** Mortar is made from sand and cement in the ratio 7:2.
If 21 buckets of sand are used, how much cement is needed?

You need to <u>multiply by 3</u> to go from 7 to 21 on the left-hand side (LHS) — so do that to <u>both sides</u>:

sand:cement
= ×3( 7:2 )×3
= 21:6

So <u>6 buckets</u> of cement are needed.

 **EXAMPLE:** Mrs Miggins owns tabby cats and ginger cats in the ratio 3:5.
All her cats are either tabby or ginger, and she has 12 tabby cats.
How many cats does Mrs Miggins have in total?

Multiply <u>both sides</u> by 4 to go from 3 to 12 on the LHS:

tabby:ginger
= ×4( 3:5 )×4
= 12:20

So Mrs Miggins has <u>12 tabby cats</u> and <u>20 ginger cats</u>.
So in total she has 12 + 20 = 32 cats

## Proportional Division

In a <u>proportional division</u> question a <u>TOTAL AMOUNT</u> is split into parts <u>in a certain ratio</u>.
The key word here is <u>PARTS</u> — concentrate on 'parts' and it all becomes quite painless:

 **EXAMPLE:** Jess, Mo and Greg share £9100 in the ratio 2:4:7. How much does Mo get?

1) <u>ADD UP THE PARTS</u>:
The ratio 2:4:7 means there will be a total of 13 <u>parts</u>:  2 + 4 + 7 = 13 parts

2) <u>DIVIDE TO FIND ONE "PART"</u>:
Just divide the <u>total amount</u> by the number of <u>parts</u>:  £9100 ÷ 13 = £700  (= 1 part)

3) <u>MULTIPLY TO FIND THE AMOUNTS</u>:
We want to know <u>Mo's share</u>, which is <u>4 parts</u>:  4 parts = 4 × £700 = £2800

## Ratio Nelson — he proportionally divided the French at Trafalgar...

Learn the rules for simplifying, how to scale ratios up and the three steps for proportional division.
Now turn over and write down what you've learned. Then try these:

Q1 Simplify: a) 28:49  b) 3.6:5.4  c) $\frac{12}{5}:\frac{21}{10}$ [4 marks]

Q2 Peanut butter and jam are mixed in the ratio 9:5.
How much peanut butter should go with 15 spoons of jam? [1 mark]

Q3 Divide 9600 in the ratio 7:5:4. [3 marks]

# Revision Questions for Section One

Well, that wraps up <u>Section One</u> — time to put yourself to the test and find out <u>how much you really know</u>.

- Try these questions and <u>tick off each one</u> when you <u>get it right</u>.
- When you've done <u>all the questions</u> for a topic and are <u>completely happy</u> with it, tick off the topic.

## Fractions (p2-3) ☑

*Don't use a calculator for questions 1-6.*

1) Simplify the following fractions: a) $\frac{9}{27}$    b) $\frac{16}{24}$    c) $\frac{36}{60}$ ☑

2) a) Write $\frac{67}{8}$ as a mixed number    b) Write $6\frac{4}{9}$ as an improper fraction ☑

3) What are the rules for multiplying, dividing and adding/subtracting fractions? ☑

4) Calculate: a) $\frac{6}{11} \times \frac{4}{5}$    b) $4\frac{2}{3} \div 1\frac{1}{4}$    c) $\frac{5}{6} - \frac{7}{10}$    d) $4\frac{5}{8} + 2\frac{3}{4}$ ☑

5) Work out $(3\frac{3}{4} - 2\frac{1}{6}) \times 2\frac{2}{3}$ ☑

6) What is $\frac{7}{8}$ of 480 g? ☑

## Fractions, Decimals and Percentages (p4) ☑

7) How do you convert: a) a fraction to a decimal?    b) a terminating decimal to a fraction? ☑

8) Write: a) 0.06 as: (i) a fraction   (ii) a percentage

        b) 35% as: (i) a fraction   (ii) a decimal ☑

        c) $\frac{11}{20}$ as: (i) a decimal   (ii) a percentage ☑

9) Write $0.5\dot{4}$ as a fraction in its simplest form.

## Percentages (p5) ☑

10) Find: a) 8% of 250 m    b) 24% of £675    c) 12.5% of 500 km ☑

11) A shop increases its prices by 5%. Find the new cost of a dress that cost £32 before the increase. ☑

12) A car was sold for £6000. After 3 years, its value has decreased by 18%.
What is the car worth after 3 years? ☑

13) Give 90 cm as a percentage of 1.54 m. Give your answer to 1 decimal place. ☑

14) What's the formula for finding a change in value as a percentage? ☑

15) The price of a house increases from £240 000 to £270 000. Find the percentage increase. ☑

16) A wrestler's weight has increased by 12% in the last year to 21.84 stone.
What was his weight a year ago? ☑

## Ratios (p6-7) ☑

17) Write each of the following ratios in its simplest form: a) 7:21    b) 24:36    c) 33:45 ☑

18) Simplify the following ratios: a) 2.8:4.2    b) $2\frac{1}{4}:\frac{15}{8}$    c) £1.25:75p ☑

19) Reduce 4:25 to the form 1:n. ☑

20) In an orchestra, the ratio of violins to flutes is 2:1. The ratio of flutes to trumpets is 5:2.
What is the ratio of violins to trumpets? Give your answer in its simplest form. ☑

21) Bob is in charge of ordering stock for a sweet shop. The shop usually sells toffees and liquorice
wheels in the ratio 7:9. Bob orders 140 toffees. How many liquorice wheels should he order? ☑

22) An ice cream van sells cones and tubs in the ratio 12:7. One day, it sells 72 cones.
How many cones and tubs does it sell in total that day? ☑

23) What are the three steps of the method of proportional division? ☑

24) Divide 4000 in the ratio 3:4:9. ☑

# Powers and Roots

**Powers** are a very useful **shorthand**:  $2 \times 2 \times 2 \times 2 \times 2 \times 2 \times 2 = 2^7$  ('two to the power 7')

That bit is easy to remember. Unfortunately, there are also <u>ten special rules</u> for powers that you need to learn.

## *The Seven Easy Rules:*

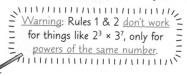

Warning: Rules 1 & 2 <u>don't work</u> for things like $2^3 \times 3^7$, only for <u>powers of the same number.</u>

1) When <u>MULTIPLYING</u>, you <u>ADD THE POWERS</u>.
   e.g. $3^4 \times 3^6 = 3^{6+4} = 3^{10}$,  $a^2 \times a^7 = a^{2+7} = a^9$

2) When <u>DIVIDING</u>, you <u>SUBTRACT THE POWERS</u>.
   e.g. $5^4 \div 5^2 = 5^{4-2} = 5^2$,  $b^8 \div b^5 = b^{8-5} = b^3$

3) When <u>RAISING</u> one power to another, you <u>MULTIPLY THEM</u>.
   e.g. $(3^2)^4 = 3^{2 \times 4} = 3^8$,  $(c^3)^6 = c^{3 \times 6} = c^{18}$

4) $x^1 = x$, <u>ANYTHING</u> to the <u>POWER 1</u> is just <u>ITSELF</u>.
   e.g. $3^1 = 3$,  $d \times d^3 = d^1 \times d^3 = d^{1+3} = d^4$

5) $x^0 = 1$, <u>ANYTHING</u> to the <u>POWER 0</u> is just <u>1</u>.
   e.g. $5^0 = 1$,  $67^0 = 1$,  $e^0 = 1$

6) $1^x = 1$, <u>1 TO ANY POWER</u> is <u>STILL JUST 1</u>.
   e.g. $1^{23} = 1$,  $1^{89} = 1$,  $1^2 = 1$

7) <u>FRACTIONS</u> — Apply the power to <u>both TOP and BOTTOM</u>.
   e.g. $\left(1\frac{3}{5}\right)^3 = \left(\frac{8}{5}\right)^3 = \frac{8^3}{5^3} = \frac{512}{125}$,  $\left(\frac{u}{v}\right)^5 = \frac{u^5}{v^5}$

## *The Three Tricky Rules:*

8) <u>NEGATIVE Powers — Turn it Upside-Down</u>

   People have real difficulty remembering this — whenever you see a negative power you need to immediately think: "Aha, that means turn it the other way up and make the power positive".

   e.g. $7^{-2} = \frac{1}{7^2} = \frac{1}{49}$,  $a^{-4} = \frac{1}{a^4}$,  $\left(\frac{3}{5}\right)^{-2} = \left(\frac{5}{3}\right)^{+2} = \frac{5^2}{3^2} = \frac{25}{9}$

9) <u>FRACTIONAL POWERS</u>

   The power $\frac{1}{2}$ means <u>Square Root</u>,
   The power $\frac{1}{3}$ means <u>Cube Root</u>,
   The power $\frac{1}{4}$ means <u>Fourth Root</u> etc.

   e.g. $25^{\frac{1}{2}} = \sqrt{25} = 5$
   $64^{\frac{1}{3}} = \sqrt[3]{64} = 4$
   $81^{\frac{1}{4}} = \sqrt[4]{81} = 3$
   $z^{\frac{1}{5}} = \sqrt[5]{z}$

   The one to really watch is when you get a <u>negative fraction</u> like $49^{-\frac{1}{2}}$ — people get mixed up and think that the minus is the square root, and forget to turn it upside down as well.

10) <u>TWO-STAGE FRACTIONAL POWERS</u>

   With fractional powers like $64^{\frac{5}{6}}$ always <u>split the fraction</u> into a <u>root</u> and a <u>power</u>, and do them in that order: <u>root</u> first, then <u>power</u>: $(64)^{\frac{1}{6} \times 5} = \left(64^{\frac{1}{6}}\right)^5 = (2)^5 = 32$.

**EXAMPLES:**

**1.** Simplify $25p^6q^5 \div 5p^2q^5$

Just deal with each bit separately:
$= (25 \div 5)(p^6 \div p^2)(q^5 \div q^5)$
$= (25 \div 5)p^{6-2}q^{5-5}$
$= 5p^4$

$q^{5-5} = q^0 = 1$

**2.** Express $\sqrt{\left(x^{\frac{9}{2}} \div x^{\frac{3}{2}}\right)}$ as a single power of $x$.

Do the bit in brackets first:
$\sqrt{\left(x^{\frac{9}{2}} \div x^{\frac{3}{2}}\right)} = \sqrt{x^{\frac{9}{2} - \frac{3}{2}}}$
$= \sqrt{x^{\frac{6}{2}}} = \sqrt{x^3}$
$= (x^3)^{\frac{1}{2}} = x^{\frac{3}{2}}$

$\sqrt{x} = x^{\frac{1}{2}}$

## *Don't let the power go to your head...*

Learn all ten exciting rules on this page, then have a go at these questions.

Q1  Simplify:  a) $(p^8)^{\frac{1}{2}}$  [1 mark]  b) $6a^4b^{-3} \times 3a^3b^5$  [2 marks]
    c) $(3x^2y^3)^3$  [2 marks]  d) $(16a^8b^{10})^{\frac{1}{2}}$  [2 marks]

Q2  Evaluate:  a) $16^{\frac{3}{4}}$  [2 marks]  b) $\left(\frac{125}{64}\right)^{-\frac{1}{3}}$  [2 marks]

Q3  Write $\frac{u^4 \times u^{\frac{7}{2}}}{(\sqrt{u})^3}$ as a single power of $u$.  [3 marks]

# Expanding Brackets

You probably know how to multiply out <u>brackets</u> by now — here are the basic types you have to deal with.

## Remove Brackets by Multiplying Them Out

### Single Brackets

$$a(b + c + d) = ab + ac + ad$$

**EXAMPLE:** Expand $3xy(x^2 + 2x - 8)$.

$$3xy(x^2 + 2x - 8) = (3xy \times x^2) + (3xy \times 2x) + (3xy \times -8)$$
$$= 3x^3y + 6x^2y - 24xy$$

### Double Brackets

$$(a + b)(c + d) = ac + ad + bc + bd$$

There's a handy way to multiply out double brackets — it's called the <u>FOIL method</u> and works like this:

<u>F</u>irst — multiply the first term in each bracket together

<u>O</u>utside — multiply the outside terms (i.e. the first term in the first bracket by the second term in the second bracket)

<u>I</u>nside — multiply the inside terms (i.e. the second term in the first bracket by the first term in the second bracket)

<u>L</u>ast — multiply the second term in each bracket together

**EXAMPLE:** Expand and simplify $(3p - 2)(5p + 3)$

$$(3p - 2)(5p + 3) = (3p \times 5p) + (3p \times 3) + (-2 \times 5p) + (-2 \times 3)$$
$$= 15p^2 + 9p - 10p - 6$$
$$= 15p^2 - p - 6$$

The two p terms <u>combine together</u>.

### Squared Brackets

$$(a + b)^2 = (a + b)(a + b) = a^2 + 2ab + b^2 \quad \text{(Just } \underline{never} \text{ make this } \underline{mistake}: (a + b)^2 = a^2 + b^2)$$

**EXAMPLE:** Expand and simplify $(2x + 7)^2$

$$(2x + 7)^2 = (2x + 7)(2x + 7)$$

Using the FOIL method
$$= 4x^2 + 14x + 14x + 49$$
$$= 4x^2 + 28x + 49$$

**EXAMPLE:** Expand and simplify $(2y^2 + 3x)^2$

$$(2y^2 + 3x)^2 = (2y^2 + 3x)(2y^2 + 3x)$$
$$= 4y^4 + 6xy^2 + 6xy^2 + 9x^2$$
$$= 4y^4 + 12xy^2 + 9x^2$$

## *Go forth and multiply out brackets...*

The FOIL method is a foolproof way of multiplying out a pair of brackets so learn it. Here's some practice:

Q1    Expand and simplify: a) $(y + 6)(y - 4)$    [2 marks]      b) $2x(x - 5 + 2y^2)$    [2 marks]

Q2    Expand and simplify: a) $(5p - 4)^2$    [2 marks]      b) $(3x^2 - 4y)^2$    [3 marks]

# Expanding Brackets

You're not quite done with multiplying out <u>brackets</u> just yet — now it's time to deal with long brackets (ones with lots of terms) and cubed brackets.

## *Deal With Long Brackets One Bit at a Time*

**LONG BRACKETS**

Write it out again with <u>each term</u> from one bracket separately multiplied by the <u>other bracket</u>.

$(x + y + z)(a + b + c + d)$
$= x(a + b + c + d) + y(a + b + c + d) + z(a + b + c + d)$
$= ax + bx + cx + dx + ay + by + cy + dy + az + bz + cz + dz$

Then <u>multiply out each</u> of these <u>brackets</u>, one at a time.

**EXAMPLE:** Expand and simplify $(x - y)(x^2 + xy + y^2)$

Multiply each term in the first bracket by the second bracket:
$(x - y)(x^2 + xy + y^2) = x(x^2 + xy + y^2) - y(x^2 + xy + y^2)$
$= (x^3 + x^2y + xy^2) - (x^2y + xy^2 + y^3)$
$= x^3 + x^2y + xy^2 - x^2y - xy^2 - y^3$
$= x^3 - y^3$

Collect like terms to simplify (watch out for the minus signs — some terms will disappear).

**EXAMPLE:** Expand and simplify $(x + y)(x^2 + 2x + 3) - x^2(x + 2y - 1)$

Multiply out the brackets...
$(x + y)(x^2 + 2x + 3) - x^2(x + 2y - 1) = x(x^2 + 2x + 3) + y(x^2 + 2x + 3) - x^2(x + 2y - 1)$
$= x^3 + 2x^2 + 3x + x^2y + 2xy + 3y - x^3 - 2x^2y + x^2$

... and collect like terms.
$= 3x^2 - x^2y + 2xy + 3x + 3y$

## *Write Out Cubed Brackets as Three Sets of Brackets*

**CUBED BRACKETS**

Write it out as <u>three sets</u> of brackets.
Multiply the <u>second</u> and <u>third</u> brackets together, then multiply the result by the <u>first</u> bracket.
Finally, <u>collect like terms</u> to simplify.

$(x + y)^3 = (x + y)(x + y)(x + y)$
$= (x + y)(x^2 + 2xy + y^2)$
$= x^3 + 2x^2y + xy^2 + x^2y + 2xy^2 + y^3$
$= x^3 + 3x^2y + 3xy^2 + y^3$

**EXAMPLE:** Expand and simplify $(x + 3)^3$

Write it out as three sets of brackets:
$(x + 3)^3 = (x + 3)(x + 3)(x + 3)$
$= (x + 3)(x^2 + 6x + 9)$
$= x^3 + 6x^2 + 9x + 3x^2 + 18x + 27$
$= x^3 + 9x^2 + 27x + 27$

This is just the product of squared brackets (like you saw on the previous page).

If you had three <u>different</u> brackets to multiply together, just multiply two sets together, then multiply by the remaining set of brackets.

## *(Learn how to)(multiply out)(cubed brackets)...*

Take your time when expanding brackets — it's easy to make a mistake and miss a term or two. Naughty.

Q1 Expand and simplify: a) $(x + 2)(x^2 + 4x - 5)$ [3 marks] b) $(a + 5)^3$ [3 marks]

12

# Factorising

Right, now you know how to expand brackets, it's time to put them back in. This is known as <u>factorising</u>.

## Common Factors Appear in Every Term

A bit which is in each term of an expression is a <u>common factor</u>.

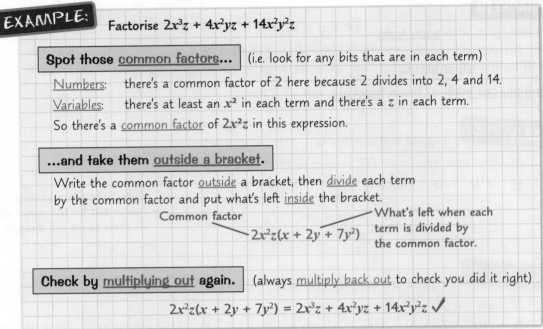

**EXAMPLE:** Factorise $2x^3z + 4x^2yz + 14x^2y^2z$

**Spot those <u>common factors</u>...** (i.e. look for any bits that are in each term)

<u>Numbers</u>: there's a common factor of 2 here because 2 divides into 2, 4 and 14.

<u>Variables</u>: there's at least an $x^2$ in each term and there's a $z$ in each term.

So there's a <u>common factor</u> of $2x^2z$ in this expression.

**...and take them <u>outside a bracket</u>.**

Write the common factor <u>outside</u> a bracket, then <u>divide</u> each term by the common factor and put what's left <u>inside</u> the bracket.

Common factor
$2x^2z(x + 2y + 7y^2)$
What's left when each term is divided by the common factor.

**Check by <u>multiplying out</u> again.** (always <u>multiply back out</u> to check you did it right)

$2x^2z(x + 2y + 7y^2) = 2x^3z + 4x^2yz + 14x^2y^2z$ ✓

But it's not just numbers and variables you need to look for — sometimes you can take out <u>whole brackets</u>.

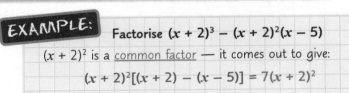

**EXAMPLE:** Factorise $(x + 2)^3 - (x + 2)^2(x - 5)$

$(x + 2)^2$ is a <u>common factor</u> — it comes out to give:

$(x + 2)^2[(x + 2) - (x - 5)] = 7(x + 2)^2$

## Look for Common Factors when Simplifying Expressions

**EXAMPLE:** Simplify $(x + 1)(x - 2) + (x + 1)^2 - x(x + 1)$

There's an $(x + 1)$ factor in each term, so we can take this out as a common factor (hurrah).

$= (x + 1)[(x - 2) + (x + 1) - x]$
$= (x + 1)(x - 2 + x + 1 - x)$
$= (x + 1)(x - 1)$
$= x^2 - 1$

It's a good idea to multiply out your brackets here to check it gives you the original expression.

## Spotting common factors — more fun than train-spotting...

As factorising is the reverse process of expanding brackets, you should always <u>check</u> your answer by multiplying out the brackets — it's a quick way of spotting mistakes (not that you'll have made any).

Q1 Factorise fully $9x^2y^2 + 15xy^2 + 12x^2y^3z^2$ [2 marks]

Q2 Factorise and simplify $(2x + 1)^2 + (2x - 1)(2x + 1) - 5(2x + 1)$ [3 marks]

Section Two — Algebra

# Factorising

If it looks like there are no common factors in an expression, it'll be tricky to factorise.
However, there are other things you can look out for that help you factorise complicated-looking expressions.

## D.O.T.S. — The Difference Of Two Squares

The 'difference of two squares' (D.O.T.S. for short) is where you have 'one thing squared' take away 'another thing squared'. There's a quick and easy way to factorise it — just use the rule below:

$$a^2 - b^2 = (a + b)(a - b)$$

**EXAMPLE:** Factorise:
a) $x^2 - 9$    Answer: $x^2 - 9 = (x + 3)(x - 3)$
b) $25p^2 - 64q^2$    Answer: $25p^2 - 64q^2 = (5p + 8q)(5p - 8q)$
     Here you had to spot that 25 and 64 are square numbers.
c) $5x^2 - 180y^2$    Answer: $5x^2 - 180y^2 = 5(x^2 - 36y^2) = 5(x + 6y)(x - 6y)$
     This time, you had to take out a factor of 5 first.

## Watch Out For Hidden Differences Of Two Squares

You might find a difference of two squares on the top or bottom of a fraction and be asked to simplify it. There's more on algebraic fractions on p.23.

**EXAMPLE:** Simplify $\dfrac{x^2 - 81}{2x + 18}$    The numerator is a difference of two squares.

$$\frac{x^2 - 81}{2x + 18} = \frac{(x + 9)(x - 9)}{2(x + 9)} = \frac{x - 9}{2}$$

Factorise the denominator.

A really sneaky way to hide a difference of two squares is to use higher powers of x. Any even power of x is another power squared — so $x^4 = (x^2)^2$, $x^6 = (x^3)^2$ etc.

**EXAMPLE:** Factorise $x^{10} - 4y^2$
$x^{10} = (x^5)^2$, so
$x^{10} - 4y^2 = (x^5 + 2y)(x^5 - 2y)$

You might have to use a difference of two squares to find a common factor when simplifying an expression.

**EXAMPLE:** Factorise fully $(m^2 - 49) + (m + 7)(2m + 3)$
The first bracket is a difference of two squares, so factorise that first:
   $(m^2 - 49) + (m + 7)(2m + 3) = (m + 7)(m - 7) + (m + 7)(2m + 3)$
Then take out the common factor...   $= (m + 7)[(m - 7) + (2m + 3)]$
... and simplify.   $= (m + 7)(3m - 4)$

## ■■ Well, one's green and one's yellow...

Make sure you can spot differences of two squares — they can be a bit sneaky but are very useful.

Q1   Factorise fully $18a^2 - 2b^2$ [3 marks]    Q2   Factorise $x^{12} - 100y^2$      [3 marks]

Q3   Simplify $\dfrac{7x - 56}{x^2 - 64}$    [3 marks]    Q4   Factorise fully $(4 - x^2) + (2 - x)(2x + 5)$ [4 marks]

# Manipulating Surds

A surd is a number like $\sqrt{2}$, or $5\sqrt{3}$ — one that's written with the $\sqrt{\phantom{x}}$ sign.

## Surds *Give an Exact Answer*

Put $\sqrt{2}$ into a calculator and you'll get something like 1.414213562... But square 1.414213562 and you get 1.999999999. And no matter how many decimal places you use, you'll never get <u>exactly</u> 2. The only way to write the exact value is to <u>use surds</u>. So if you're asked for an exact answer, leave your answer as a <u>surd</u>.

## *There are Three Main Rules for Using Surds*

There are three <u>rules</u> you'll need to know to be able to use surds properly:

**1** $\sqrt{a} \times \sqrt{b} = \sqrt{a \times b}$     **2** $\dfrac{\sqrt{a}}{\sqrt{b}} = \sqrt{\dfrac{a}{b}}$     **3** $a = (\sqrt{a})^2 = \sqrt{a}\sqrt{a}$

<u>Simplifying</u> surds means making the number in the $\sqrt{\phantom{x}}$ sign <u>smaller</u>, getting rid of a <u>fraction</u> in the $\sqrt{\phantom{x}}$ sign or <u>combining</u> different surds that can be written with the <u>same number</u> in the square root.

**EXAMPLE:** Simplify:   a) $\sqrt{12}$

Use rule 1: $\sqrt{12} = \sqrt{4 \times 3}$
$= \sqrt{4} \times \sqrt{3} = 2\sqrt{3}$

b) $\sqrt{\dfrac{3}{16}}$

Use rule 2: $\sqrt{\dfrac{3}{16}} = \dfrac{\sqrt{3}}{\sqrt{16}} = \dfrac{\sqrt{3}}{4}$

**EXAMPLE:** Write $\sqrt{300} + \sqrt{48} - 2\sqrt{75}$ in the form $a\sqrt{3}$, where $a$ is an integer.

Write each surd in terms of $\sqrt{3}$: $\sqrt{300} = \sqrt{100 \times 3} = \sqrt{100} \times \sqrt{3} = 10\sqrt{3}$
$\sqrt{48} = \sqrt{16 \times 3} = \sqrt{16} \times \sqrt{3} = 4\sqrt{3}$
$2\sqrt{75} = 2\sqrt{25 \times 3} = 2 \times \sqrt{25} \times \sqrt{3} = 10\sqrt{3}$

Then do the sum (remember to leave your answer in terms of $\sqrt{3}$):
$\sqrt{300} + \sqrt{48} - 2\sqrt{75} = 10\sqrt{3} + 4\sqrt{3} - 10\sqrt{3}$
$= 4\sqrt{3}$

## *Rationalise the Denominator to Simplify Fractions*

Surds are the last thing you want on the bottom of a fraction.
To get rid of them, you have to <u>rationalise the denominator</u>...

**EXAMPLE:** Write $\dfrac{3}{2 + \sqrt{5}}$ in the form $a + b\sqrt{5}$, where $a$ and $b$ are integers.

To rationalise the denominator, multiply top and bottom by $2 - \sqrt{5}$:

$\dfrac{3}{2 + \sqrt{5}} = \dfrac{3(2 - \sqrt{5})}{(2 + \sqrt{5})(2 - \sqrt{5})} = \dfrac{6 - 3\sqrt{5}}{2^2 - 2\sqrt{5} + 2\sqrt{5} - (\sqrt{5})^2}$

$= \dfrac{6 - 3\sqrt{5}}{4 - 5} = \dfrac{6 - 3\sqrt{5}}{-1} = -6 + 3\sqrt{5}$    (so $a = -6$ and $b = 3$)

> For denominators of the form $a \pm \sqrt{b}$, you always multiply by the denominator, but <u>change the sign</u> in front of the surd.

## *Rationalise the denominator? How absurd...*

Don't make the mistake of thinking that $\sqrt{a} + \sqrt{b} = \sqrt{a + b}$ — this is very wrong indeed.

Q1   Write $(3 + \sqrt{5})(5 - \sqrt{5})$ in the form $a + b\sqrt{5}$, where $a$ and $b$ are integers.     [2 marks]

Q2   Write $\dfrac{2}{2 + \sqrt{3}}$ in the form $a + b\sqrt{3}$, where $a$ and $b$ are integers.     [3 marks]

# Solving Equations

You should know the basics of <u>solving equations</u> — I've put it all together into a handy step-by-step method.

## Solving Equations Using the 6-Step Method

Here's the method to follow (just ignore any steps that don't apply to your equation):

1) Get rid of any <u>fractions</u>.
2) <u>Multiply out</u> any brackets.
3) Collect all the <u>x-terms</u> on one side and all <u>non x-terms</u> on the other.
4) Reduce it to the form '<u>Ax = B</u>' (by <u>combining like terms</u>). You might have to do some <u>factorising</u> here too.

> A and B could be numbers or letters (or a mix of both).

5) <u>Divide both sides by A</u> to give 'x =    '.
6) If you're left with '$x^2 =$    ', <u>square root</u> both sides to get 'x = ±    ' (<u>don't forget</u> the ±).

**EXAMPLE:** Solve $\dfrac{7x+3}{4} - \dfrac{6x+2}{5} = 2$

Multiply everything by 4 then by 5.

1) Get rid of any <u>fractions</u>.  (×4), (×5)  $\dfrac{4 \times 5 \times (7x+3)}{4} - \dfrac{4 \times 5 \times (6x+2)}{5} = 4 \times 5 \times 2$

$$5(7x+3) - 4(6x+2) = 40$$

2) <u>Multiply out</u> any brackets.  $35x + 15 - 24x - 8 = 40$

3) Collect all the <u>x-terms</u> on one side and all <u>number terms</u> on the other.

(–15), (+8)  $35x - 24x = 40 - 15 + 8$

4) Reduce it to the form '<u>Ax = B</u>' (by <u>combining like terms</u>).

$11x = 33$

5) Finally <u>divide both sides by A</u> to give 'x =    ', and that's your answer.

(÷11)  $x = 3$  (You're left with 'x =    ' so you can ignore step 6.)

## Dealing With Squares

If you're unlucky, you might get an <u>x²</u> in an equation. If this happens, you'll end up with '$x^2 = \dots$' at step 5, and then step 6 is to take <u>square roots</u>. There's one very important thing to remember: whenever you take the square root of a number, the answer can be <u>positive</u> or <u>negative</u>...

**EXAMPLE:** Solve $3x^2 = 48$.

(÷3)  $x^2 = 16$
(√)  $x = \pm 4$

> You always get a <u>+ve</u> and <u>-ve</u> version of the <u>same number</u> (your calculator only gives the +ve answer). This shows why:
> $4^2 = 4 \times 4 = 16$ but also
> $(-4)^2 = (-4) \times (-4) = 16$.

## Square Roots? Must be a geomer-tree...*

Learn the 6-step method, then try these questions.

Q1    Solve $5x^2 + 7 = 187$    [2 marks]        Q2    Solve $\dfrac{3x+4}{5} + \dfrac{4x-1}{3} = 14$    [3 marks]

*winner of Best Maths Gag in a Supporting Role, International Algebra Awards 2014

# Rearranging Formulas

Rearranging formulas means making one letter the subject, e.g. getting 'y = ' from '2x + z = 3(y + 2p)' — you have to get the subject on its own. Rearranging formulas is remarkably similar to solving equations. The method is identical to the method for solving equations on the previous page, except there might be an extra step — if the subject appears in a square root, you'll need to square both sides to get rid of it.

## What To Do If...

### ...the Subject Appears in a Fraction

You won't always need to use all the steps in the method — just ignore the ones that don't apply.

**EXAMPLE:** Make b the subject of the formula $a = \dfrac{3b + 2}{5}$.

1) **Get rid of any fractions.** (by multiplying every term by 5, the denominator)

$(\times 5)$  $5a = \dfrac{5(3b + 2)}{5}$

$5a = 3b + 2$

There aren't any brackets so ignore step 2.

3) **Collect all the subject terms on one side and all non-subject terms on the other.**

(remember that you're trying to make b the subject)    $(-2)$  $3b = 5a - 2$

4) **It's now in $\underline{Ax = B}$ form.** (where A = 3 and B = 5a − 2)

5) **Divide both sides by 3 to give 'b =     '.**    $(\div 3)$  $b = \dfrac{5a - 2}{3}$

b isn't squared, so you don't need step 6.

### ...there's a Square or Square Root Involved

If the subject appears as a square or in a square root, you'll have to do the opposite to get rid of it.

**EXAMPLE:** Make v the subject of the formula $u = 2v^2 + 7w$.

There aren't any fractions or brackets so ignore steps 1-2 (this is pretty easy so far).

3) **Collect all the subject terms on one side and all non-subject terms on the other.**

$(-7w)$  $2v^2 = u - 7w$

4) **It's now in $\underline{Ax^2 = B}$ form.** (where A = 2 and B = u − 7w)

5) **Divide both sides by 2 to give '$v^2 = $     '.**    $(\div 2)$  $v^2 = \dfrac{u - 7w}{2}$

6) **Square root both sides to get '$v = \pm$     '.**    $(\sqrt{\ })$  $v = \pm\sqrt{\dfrac{u - 7w}{2}}$    *Don't forget the ±!*

**EXAMPLE:** Make n the subject of the formula $m = \sqrt{n - 8}$.

**Get rid of any square roots by squaring both sides.**    $m^2 = n - 8$

There aren't any fractions or brackets so ignore steps 1-2.

3) **Collect all the subject terms on one side and all non-subject terms on the other.**

$(+8)$    $n = m^2 + 8$    This is in the form 'n =     ' so you don't need to do steps 4-6.

# Rearranging Formulas

Carrying straight on from the previous page, now it's time for what to do if...

## ...the Subject Appears Twice

Go home and cry. No, not really — you'll just have to do some <u>factorising</u>, usually in step 4.

**EXAMPLE:** Make p the subject of the formula $q = \dfrac{2p + 3}{p - 2}$.

1) **Get rid of any <u>fractions</u>.** $\quad q(p - 2) = 2p + 3$

2) **<u>Multiply out</u> any brackets.** $\quad pq - 2q = 2p + 3$

3) **Collect all the <u>subject terms</u> on one side and all <u>non-subject terms</u> on the other.**
$$pq - 2p = 2q + 3$$

4) **Reduce it to '<u>Ax = B</u>' form by <u>factorising</u>.** $\quad p(q - 2) = 2q + 3$
$\qquad$ *p was in both terms on the LHS so it comes out as a common factor.*

5) **<u>Divide both sides by (q – 2)</u> to give 'p =    '.** $\quad p = \dfrac{2q + 3}{q - 2}$ (p isn't squared, so you don't need step 6.)

## ...there's More Than One Fraction

This can be a tricky one — you have to multiply <u>everything</u> by the <u>common denominator</u>, which often leaves you with something that's a bit nasty to rearrange. The <u>6-step method</u> still works though.

**EXAMPLE:** Make r the subject of the formula $\dfrac{1}{t} = \dfrac{1}{2s} - \dfrac{2}{r}$.

1) **Get rid of any <u>fractions</u>.** (by multiplying every term by 2rst, the common denominator)
$\qquad$ $(\times 2rst)\quad \dfrac{2rst}{t} = \dfrac{2rst}{2s} - \dfrac{2(2rst)}{r}$
$\qquad\qquad 2rs = rt - 4st$

There aren't any brackets so ignore step 2.

3) **Collect all the <u>subject terms</u> on one side and all <u>non-subject terms</u> on the other.**
$$rt - 2rs = 4st$$

4) **Reduce it to '<u>Ax = B</u>' form by <u>factorising</u>.** $\quad r(t - 2s) = 4st$

5) **<u>Divide both sides by (t – 2s)</u> to give 'r =    '.** $\quad r = \dfrac{4st}{t - 2s}$ (r isn't squared, so you don't need step 6.)

## ...there's a pirate invasion — hide in a cupboard...

Now you know all the tricks of the trade, it's time to get rearrangin' with these snazzy questions:

Q1 $\quad$ Make $q$ the subject of the formula $p = \dfrac{q}{4} - 3r$ $\hfill$ [2 marks]

Q2 $\quad$ Make $z$ the subject of the formula $x = \dfrac{y - 3z}{2}$ $\hfill$ [2 marks]

Q3 $\quad$ Make $y$ the subject of: a) $x = \dfrac{y^2}{9}$ $\quad$ [2 marks] $\qquad$ b) $x = \dfrac{2y}{y + z}$ $\hfill$ [4 marks]

Q4 $\quad$ Make $a$ the subject of the formula $3a + 7 = 2b(a - 4)$ $\hfill$ [3 marks]

# Factorising Quadratics

There are several ways of solving a quadratic equation as detailed on the following pages. You need to know all the methods as they sometimes ask for specific ones in the exam.

## Factorising a Quadratic

1) 'Factorising a quadratic' means 'putting it into 2 brackets'.

2) The standard format for quadratic equations is:   $ax^2 + bx + c = 0$.

3) This page gives you the method for when $\underline{a = 1}$.   E.g.   $x^2 + 3x + 2 = 0$   *See next page for when 'a' is not 1.*

4) As well as factorising a quadratic, you might be asked to solve it. This just means finding the values of x that make each bracket $\underline{0}$ (see example below).

## Factorising Method when a = 1

1) ALWAYS rearrange into the STANDARD FORMAT: $ax^2 + bx + c = 0$.

2) Write down the TWO BRACKETS with the x's in: $(x\quad)(x\quad) = 0$.

3) Then find 2 numbers that MULTIPLY to give 'c' (the end number) but also ADD/SUBTRACT to give 'b' (the coefficient of x).   *Ignore any minus signs at this stage.*

4) Fill in the +/− signs and make sure they work out properly.

5) As an ESSENTIAL CHECK, expand the brackets to make sure they give the original equation.

6) Finally, SOLVE THE EQUATION by setting each bracket equal to 0.

You only need to do step 6) if the question asks you to solve the quadratic — if it just tells you to factorise, you can stop at step 5).

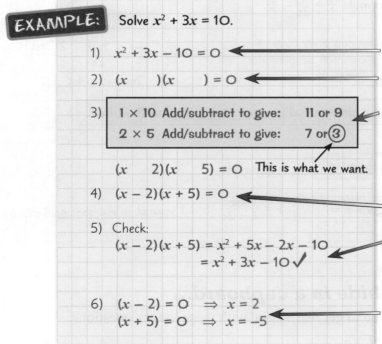

**EXAMPLE:** Solve $x^2 + 3x = 10$.

1) $x^2 + 3x - 10 = 0$

2) $(x\quad)(x\quad) = 0$

3) 
| $1 \times 10$ Add/subtract to give: | 11 or 9 |
| $2 \times 5$ Add/subtract to give: | 7 or ③ |

$(x\quad 2)(x\quad 5) = 0$   This is what we want.

4) $(x - 2)(x + 5) = 0$

5) Check:
$(x - 2)(x + 5) = x^2 + 5x - 2x - 10$
$= x^2 + 3x - 10$ ✓

6) $(x - 2) = 0 \Rightarrow x = 2$
$(x + 5) = 0 \Rightarrow x = -5$

1) Rearrange into the standard format.

2) Write down the initial brackets.

3) Find the right pairs of numbers that multiply to give c (= 10), and add or subtract to give b (= 3) (remember, we're ignoring the +/− signs for now).

4) Now fill in the +/− signs so that 2 and 5 add/subtract to give 3 (= b).

5) ESSENTIAL check — EXPAND the brackets to make sure they give the original equation.

But we're not finished yet — we've only factorised it, we still need to...

6) SOLVE THE EQUATION by setting each bracket equal to 0.

## Bring me a biscuit or I'll factorise your quadratic...

Handy tip: to help you work out which signs you need, look at c. If c is positive, the signs will be the same (both positive or both negative), but if c is negative the signs will be different (one positive and one negative).

Q1   Factorise $x^2 - 4x - 21$   [2 marks]          Q2   Solve $x^2 - 9x + 18 = 0$   [3 marks]

# Factorising Quadratics

So far so good.  It gets a bit more complicated when 'a' isn't 1, but it's all good fun, right?  Right?  Well, I think it's fun anyway.

## When 'a' is Not 1

The basic method is still the same but it's <u>a bit messier</u> — the initial brackets are <u>different</u> as the first terms in each bracket have to multiply to give '<u>a</u>'.  This means finding the <u>other</u> numbers to go in the brackets is harder as there are more <u>combinations</u> to try.  The best way to get to grips with it is to have a look at an <u>example</u>.

**EXAMPLE:**  Solve $3x^2 - 2x - 8 = 0$.

1)  $3x^2 - 2x - 8 = 0$

2)  $(3x\ \ )(x\ \ ) = 0$

3)  Number pairs: $1 \times 8$  and  $2 \times 4$

$(3x\ \ 1)(x\ \ 8)$ <u>multiplies</u> to give <u>24x and 1x</u> which <u>add/subtract</u> to give <u>25x or 23x</u>

$(3x\ \ 8)(x\ \ 1)$ <u>multiplies</u> to give <u>3x and 8x</u> which <u>add/subtract</u> to give <u>11x or 5x</u>

$(3x\ \ 2)(x\ \ 4)$ <u>multiplies</u> to give <u>12x and 2x</u> which <u>add/subtract</u> to give <u>14x or 10x</u>

$(3x\ \ 4)(x\ \ 2)$ <u>multiplies</u> to give <u>6x and 4x</u> which <u>add/subtract</u> to give <u>10x or (2x)</u> ✓

$(3x\ \ 4)(x\ \ 2)$

4)  $(3x + 4)(x - 2)$

5)  $(3x + 4)(x - 2) = 3x^2 - 6x + 4x - 8$
$= 3x^2 - 2x - 8$ ✓

6)  $(3x + 4) = 0 \Rightarrow x = -\frac{4}{3}$
$(x - 2) = 0 \Rightarrow x = 2$

1)  <u>Rearrange</u> into the standard format.

2)  Write down the <u>initial brackets</u> — this time, one of the brackets will have a <u>3x</u> in it.

3)  The <u>tricky part</u>: first, find <u>pairs of numbers</u> that <u>multiply to give c</u> (= 8), ignoring the minus sign for now.

Then, <u>try out</u> the number pairs you just found in the brackets until you find one that gives 2x.  But remember, each pair of numbers has to be tried in <u>2 positions</u> (as the brackets are different — one has 3x in it).

4)  <u>Now fill in the +/− signs</u> so that 6 and 4 add/subtract to give −2 (= b).

5)  <u>ESSENTIAL check</u> — <u>EXPAND the brackets</u>.

6)  <u>SOLVE THE EQUATION</u> by setting each bracket <u>equal to 0</u> (if a isn't 1, one of your answers might be a <u>fraction</u>).

**EXAMPLE:**  Solve $2x^2 + 7 = 15x$.

1)  Put in standard format: $2x^2 - 15x + 7 = 0$

2)  Initial brackets: $(2x\ \ )(x\ \ ) = 0$

3)  Number pairs: $1 \times 7$

$(2x\ \ 7)(x\ \ 1)$ <u>multiplies</u> to give <u>2x and 7x</u> which <u>add/subtract</u> to give <u>9x or 5x</u>

$(2x\ \ 1)(x\ \ 7)$ <u>multiplies</u> to give <u>14x and 1x</u> which <u>add/subtract</u> to give <u>(15x)</u> or 13x

$(2x\ \ 1)(x\ \ 7)$ ✓

4)  Put in the signs: $(2x - 1)(x - 7)$

5)  Check:
$(2x - 1)(x - 7) = 2x^2 - 14x - x + 7$
$= 2x^2 - 15x + 7$ ✓

6)  Solve:
$(2x - 1) = 0 \Rightarrow x = \frac{1}{2}$
$(x - 7) = 0 \Rightarrow x = 7$

## *It's not scary — just think of it as brackets giving algebra a hug ...*

Learn the step-by-step method for solving quadratics, then have a go at these Exam Practice Questions.

Q1  Factorise $2x^2 - 7x - 15$  [2 marks]

Q2  Solve $3x^2 + 13x - 10 = 0$  [3 marks]

Q3  Factorise $3x^2 + 25x + 28$  [2 marks]

Q4  Solve $5x^2 - 11x = 12$  [3 marks]

# The Quadratic Formula

The solutions to ANY quadratic equation $ax^2 + bx + c = 0$ are given by this formula:

$$x = \frac{-b \pm \sqrt{b^2 - 4ac}}{2a}$$

<u>LEARN THIS FORMULA</u> — and <u>how to use it</u>. It's usually given in the exam, but if you don't learn it, you won't know how to use it. Using it isn't that hard, but there are a few pitfalls — so <u>TAKE HEED of these crucial details</u>:

## *Quadratic Formula — Five Crucial Details*

1) Take it nice and slowly — always write it down in stages as you go.

2) WHENEVER YOU GET A MINUS SIGN, <u>THE ALARM BELLS SHOULD ALWAYS RING</u>!

If either 'a' or 'c' is negative, the $-4ac$ effectively becomes $+4ac$, so watch out. Also, be careful if b is negative, as $-b$ will be positive.

3) Remember it's <u>2a</u> on the bottom line, not just a — and you <u>divide ALL of the top line by 2a</u>.

4) The $\pm$ sign means you end up with <u>two solutions</u> (by replacing it in the final step with '+' and '–').

5) If you get a <u>negative</u> number inside your square root, go back and <u>check your working</u>. Some quadratics do have a negative value in the square root, but they won't come up in your exam.

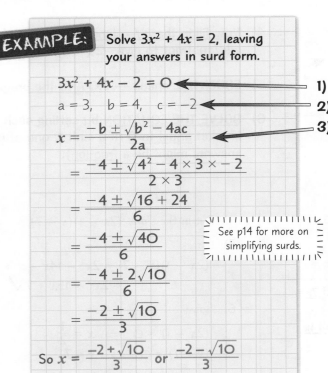

**EXAMPLE:** Solve $3x^2 + 4x = 2$, leaving your answers in surd form.

$3x^2 + 4x - 2 = 0$

$a = 3, \quad b = 4, \quad c = -2$

$x = \dfrac{-b \pm \sqrt{b^2 - 4ac}}{2a}$

$= \dfrac{-4 \pm \sqrt{4^2 - 4 \times 3 \times -2}}{2 \times 3}$

$= \dfrac{-4 \pm \sqrt{16 + 24}}{6}$

$= \dfrac{-4 \pm \sqrt{40}}{6}$

$= \dfrac{-4 \pm 2\sqrt{10}}{6}$

$= \dfrac{-2 \pm \sqrt{10}}{3}$

So $x = \dfrac{-2 + \sqrt{10}}{3}$ or $\dfrac{-2 - \sqrt{10}}{3}$

See p14 for more on simplifying surds.

1) First get it into the form <u>$ax^2 + bx + c = 0$</u>.
2) Then carefully identify a, b and c.
3) Put these values into the quadratic formula and <u>write down each stage</u>.

**When to use the quadratic formula:**

- If you have a quadratic that <u>won't</u> easily <u>factorise</u>.
- If the question mentions <u>decimal places</u> or <u>significant figures</u>.
- If the question asks for <u>surds</u> (though this could be completing the square instead — see next page).

## *Enough number crunches? Now it's time to work on your quads...*

Learn the crucial details and how to use the Quadratic Formula. Done it? Now it's time to practise your mad new skillz with these handy Exam Practice Questions...

Q1    Solve $x^2 + 13x - 3 = 0$, giving your answers to 2 decimal places.     [3 marks]

Q2    Solve $2x^2 - 6x = 9$, leaving your answers in surd form.     [3 marks]

# Completing the Square

There's just one more method to learn for <u>solving quadratics</u> — and it's a bit of a nasty one. It's called '<u>completing the square</u>', and takes a bit to get your head round it.

## *Solving Quadratics by 'Completing the Square'*

To 'complete the square' you have to:

    1) Write down a <u>SQUARED</u> bracket, and then    2) Stick a number on the end to '<u>COMPLETE</u>' it.

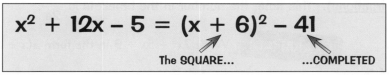

$$x^2 + 12x - 5 = (x + 6)^2 - 41$$

The SQUARE...       ...COMPLETED

It's not that bad if you learn all the steps — some of them aren't all that obvious.

1) As always, <u>REARRANGE THE QUADRATIC INTO THE STANDARD FORMAT</u>: $ax^2 + bx + c$ (the rest of this method is for $a = 1$).

2) <u>WRITE OUT THE INITIAL BRACKET</u>: $(x + \frac{b}{2})^2$ — just divide the value of b by **2**.

3) <u>MULTIPLY OUT THE BRACKETS</u> and <u>COMPARE TO THE ORIGINAL</u> to find what you need to add or subtract to complete the square.

4) Add or subtract the <u>ADJUSTING NUMBER</u> to make it <u>MATCH THE ORIGINAL</u>.

> If a isn't 1, you have to divide through by 'a' or take out a factor of 'a' at the start — see next page.

**EXAMPLE:**

a) Express $x^2 + 14x + 22$ in the form $(x + m)^2 + n$.

1) It's in the <u>standard format</u>.      $x^2 + 14x + 22$

2) Write out the <u>initial bracket</u>      $(x + 7)^2$      Original equation had +22 here...

3) Multiply out the brackets and <u>compare</u> to the original.      $(x + 7)^2 = x^2 + 14x + 49$

     $(x + 7)^2 - 27 = x^2 + 14x + 49 - 27$    ...so you need -27

4) Subtract <u>adjusting number</u> (27).      $= x^2 + 14x + 22 \checkmark$ —— matches original now!

So the completed square is: $(x + 7)^2 - 27$.

Now <u>use</u> the completed square to solve the equation. There are <u>three more steps</u> for this:

b) Hence solve $x^2 + 14x + 22 = 0$, leaving your answers in simplified surd form.

1) Put the number on the other side (+27).      $(x + 7)^2 - 27 = 0$

     $(x + 7)^2 = 27$

2) Square root both sides (don't forget the ±!) ($\sqrt{\ }$).      $x + 7 = \pm\sqrt{27}$

     $x = -7 \pm 3\sqrt{3}$

3) Get x on its own (–7).      So the two solutions (in surd form) are:

$$x = -7 + 3\sqrt{3} \text{ and } x = -7 - 3\sqrt{3}$$

## *But if a square's not complete, is it really a square...?*

Go over this carefully, 'cos it's pretty gosh darn confusing at first. Learn the method for completing the square, and brush up on your equation-solving skills too. Then try these questions...

Q1     Write $x^2 - 16x + 11$ in the form $(x + p)^2 + q$.                [2 marks]

Q2     Solve $x^2 + 8x + 10 = 0$, by first writing it in the form $(x + m)^2 + n = 0$.
         Give your answers in the form $a \pm \sqrt{b}$, where $a$ and $b$ are integers.      [4 marks]

# Completing the Square

If you're a fan of <u>completing the square</u>, good news — there's another page on it here.
If you're not a fan of completing the square, bad news — there's another page on it here.

## Completing the Square When 'a' Isn't 1

If 'a' isn't 1, completing the square is a bit trickier. You follow the <u>same method</u> as on the previous page, but you have to take out a <u>factor of 'a'</u> from the $x^2$ and x-terms before you start (which often means you end up with awkward <u>fractions</u>). This time, the number in the brackets is $\frac{b}{2a}$.

**EXAMPLE:** Write $2x^2 + 5x + 9$ in the form $a(x + m)^2 + n$.

1) It's in the <u>standard format</u>. ———— $2x^2 + 5x + 9$

2) Take out a <u>factor</u> of 2. ———— $2(x^2 + \frac{5}{2}x) + 9$

*Original equation had +9 here...*

3) Write out the <u>initial bracket</u>. ———— $2(x + \frac{5}{4})^2$

4) Multiply out the brackets and <u>compare</u> to the original. ———— $2(x + \frac{5}{4})^2 = 2x^2 + 5x + \frac{25}{8}$

*...so you need*

5) Add on <u>adjusting number</u> ($\frac{47}{8}$). ———— $2(x + \frac{5}{4})^2 + \frac{47}{8} = 2x^2 + 5x + \frac{25}{8} + \frac{47}{8}$

$9 - \frac{25}{8} = \frac{47}{8}$

$= 2x^2 + 5x + 9$ ✓ *matches original now!*

So the completed square is: $2(x + \frac{5}{4})^2 + \frac{47}{8}$

## The Completed Square Tells You Things About the Graph

There's more about <u>sketching</u> quadratic graphs on p41, but you can use the <u>completed square</u> to work out key details about the graph.

1) For a <u>positive</u> quadratic (where the $x^2$ coefficient is positive), the <u>adjusting number</u> tells you the <u>minimum</u> y-value of the graph. If the completed square is $(x + a)^2 + b$, this minimum y-value will occur when the brackets are equal to 0 (because the bit in brackets is squared, so is never negative) — i.e. when $x = -a$.

2) The <u>solutions</u> to the equation tell you where the graph <u>crosses</u> the <u>x-axis</u>. If the adjusting number is <u>positive</u>, the graph will <u>never</u> cross the x-axis as it will always be greater than 0 (this means that the quadratic has <u>no real roots</u>).

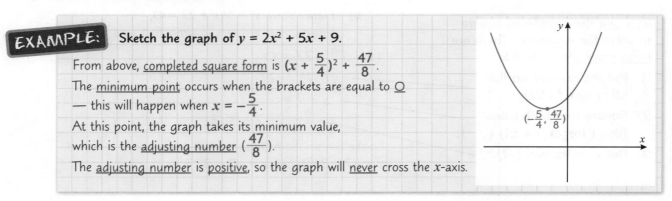

**EXAMPLE:** Sketch the graph of $y = 2x^2 + 5x + 9$.

From above, <u>completed square form</u> is $(x + \frac{5}{4})^2 + \frac{47}{8}$.

The <u>minimum point</u> occurs when the brackets are equal to 0 — this will happen when $x = -\frac{5}{4}$.

At this point, the graph takes its minimum value, which is the <u>adjusting number</u> ($\frac{47}{8}$).

The <u>adjusting number</u> is <u>positive</u>, so the graph will <u>never</u> cross the x-axis.

$(-\frac{5}{4}, \frac{47}{8})$

## Complete the following square: ☐

I'm not going to lie, this page was rather challenging (I got a bit confused myself). Be careful taking out the factor of $a$ — you only do it for the first two terms. Take care with your fractions too.

Q1 a) Write $2x^2 + 3x - 5$ in the form $a(x + b)^2 + c$. [4 marks]

b) Hence solve $2x^2 + 3x - 5 = 0$. [2 marks]

c) Use your answers to parts a) and b) to find the coordinates of the minimum point of the graph of $y = 2x^2 + 3x - 5$ and state where the graph crosses the x-axis. [2 marks]

# Algebraic Fractions

Unfortunately, fractions aren't limited to numbers — you can get <u>algebraic fractions</u> too. Fortunately, everything you learnt about fractions on p2-3 can be applied to algebraic fractions as well.

## Simplifying Algebraic Fractions

You can <u>simplify</u> algebraic fractions by <u>cancelling</u> terms on the top and bottom — just deal with each <u>letter</u> individually and cancel as much as you can. You might have to <u>factorise</u> first (see pages 12-13 and 18-19).

**EXAMPLES:**

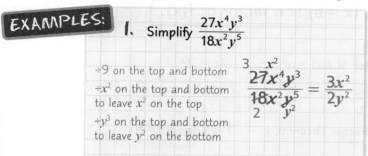

**1.** Simplify $\dfrac{27x^4y^3}{18x^2y^5}$

$\div9$ on the top and bottom

$\div x^2$ on the top and bottom to leave $x^2$ on the top

$\div y^3$ on the top and bottom to leave $y^2$ on the bottom

$$\dfrac{27x^4y^3}{18x^2y^5} = \dfrac{3x^2}{2y^2}$$

**2.** Simplify $\dfrac{x^2 - 36}{x^2 + 3x - 18}$

Factorise the top using D.O.T.S.

Factorise the quadratic on the bottom

$$\dfrac{(x+6)(x-6)}{(x-3)(x+6)} = \dfrac{x-6}{x-3}$$

Then cancel the common factor of $(x + 6)$

## Multiplying/Dividing Algebraic Fractions

1) To <u>multiply</u> two fractions, just multiply tops and bottoms <u>separately</u>.

2) To <u>divide</u>, turn the second fraction <u>upside down</u> then <u>multiply</u>.

**EXAMPLE:** Simplify $\dfrac{x^2 - 4}{x^2 + x - 12} \div \dfrac{2x + 4}{x^2 - 3x}$

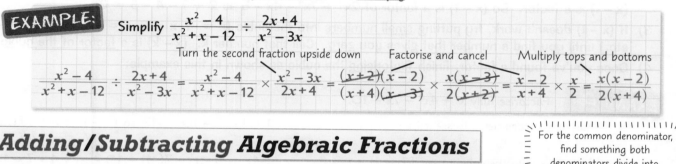

Turn the second fraction upside down · Factorise and cancel · Multiply tops and bottoms

$$\dfrac{x^2-4}{x^2+x-12} \div \dfrac{2x+4}{x^2-3x} = \dfrac{x^2-4}{x^2+x-12} \times \dfrac{x^2-3x}{2x+4} = \dfrac{(x+2)(x-2)}{(x+4)(x-3)} \times \dfrac{x(x-3)}{2(x+2)} = \dfrac{x-2}{x+4} \times \dfrac{x}{2} = \dfrac{x(x-2)}{2(x+4)}$$

## Adding/Subtracting Algebraic Fractions

<u>Adding</u> or <u>subtracting</u> is a bit more difficult:

1) Work out the <u>common denominator</u> (see p3).

2) Multiply <u>top and bottom</u> of each fraction by whatever gives you the common denominator.

3) Add or subtract the <u>numerators</u> only.

For the common denominator, find something both denominators divide into.

| Fractions | | |
|---|---|---|
| $\dfrac{1}{x} + \dfrac{1}{3x}$ | $\dfrac{1}{x+1} + \dfrac{1}{x-2}$ | $\dfrac{1}{x} + \dfrac{1}{x(x+1)}$ |
| $3x$ | $(x+1)(x-2)$ | $x(x+1)$ |

Common denominator

**EXAMPLE:** Write $\dfrac{2}{(x+1)} + \dfrac{1}{(x-4)}$ as a single fraction.

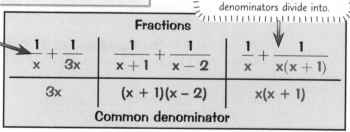

1st fraction: × top & bottom by $(x - 4)$

2nd fraction: × top & bottom by $(x + 1)$

$$\dfrac{2}{(x+1)} + \dfrac{1}{(x-4)} = \dfrac{2(x-4)}{(x+1)(x-4)} + \dfrac{(x+1)}{(x+1)(x-4)}$$

Common denominator will be $(x+1)(x-4)$

Add the numerators

$$= \dfrac{2x-8}{(x+1)(x-4)} + \dfrac{x+1}{(x+1)(x-4)} = \dfrac{3x-7}{(x+1)(x-4)}$$

## I'd like to cancel the Summer Term...

One more thing... never do this: $\dfrac{x}{x+y} = \dfrac{1}{y}$ ✗ It's wrong wrong WRONG! Got that? Good, now try these:

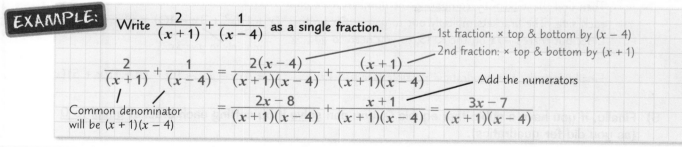

Q1    Simplify $\dfrac{x^4 - 4y^2}{x^3 - 2xy}$  [2 marks]    Q2    Simplify $\dfrac{x^2 - 3x - 10}{x^3 - 2x^2} \div \dfrac{x^2 - 25}{6x - 12}$  [5 marks]

Q3    Write $\dfrac{2}{x+5} + \dfrac{3}{x-2}$ as a single fraction in its simplest form.    [3 marks]

# Factorising Cubics

You should be a dab hand at factorising quadratics by now — so it's time to move things up a gear and learn how to factorise <u>cubics</u>. Remember, a cubic is an expression of the form $ax^3 + bx^2 + cx + d$.

## The Factor Theorem Helps You To Factorise Cubics

Using <u>function notation</u> (see p39-40), the <u>Factor Theorem</u> says:

> If $f(x)$ is a cubic, and $f(a) = 0$, then $(x - a)$ is a factor of $f(x)$.

*In other words: if you know the roots, you also know the factors — and vice versa.*

**EXAMPLE:** Show that $(x - 2)$ is a factor of $f(x) = x^3 + 5x^2 - 2x - 24$.

All you have to do here is show that $f(2) = 0$, so put $x = 2$ into the expression for $f(x)$:

$$f(2) = (2)^3 + 5(2)^2 - 2(2) - 24 = 8 + 20 - 4 - 24 = 0$$

$f(x) = 0$ when $x = 2$, so by the Factor Theorem, $(x - 2)$ is a factor of $f(x)$.

## Use Trial and Error to Factorise Cubics

1) If the question doesn't give you any <u>factors</u>, the best way to find a factor is to use <u>trial and error</u>.

2) The first factor to try is $(x - 1)$. There's a quick way of checking this — if all the coefficients <u>add up to 0</u>, $(x - 1)$ is a factor. So $(x - 1)$ is a factor of $2x^3 + 7x^2 - 4x - 5$ as $2 + 7 - 4 - 5 = 0$.

3) If $(x - 1)$ doesn't work, try putting <u>small numbers</u> into the cubic ($x = -1$, $x = 2$, $x = -2$, $x = 3$, $x = -3$ etc.) until you find a number that gives you <u>zero</u>. Call that number $k$. $(x - k)$ is a <u>factor of the cubic</u>.

4) Once you've found a factor, finish <u>factorising</u> the cubic as shown in this example:

**EXAMPLE:** Factorise fully $x^3 + 4x^2 - 7x - 10$.

Add up the coefficients to see if $(x - 1)$ is a factor:

$1 + 4 - 7 - 10 = -12$, so $(x - 1)$ is <u>not</u> a factor.

Put $x = -1$ into the cubic to see if $(x + 1)$ is a factor:

$(-1)^3 + 4(-1)^2 - 7(-1) - 10 = -1 + 4 + 7 - 10$
$= 0$, so $(x + 1)$ <u>is a factor</u>.

Now you want to find a <u>quadratic factor</u>. Write down the factor you know, along with another set of <u>brackets</u>:

$(x + 1)( \qquad ) = x^3 + 4x^2 - 7x - 10$

Fill in the $x^2$-term and the <u>number term</u>:

$(x + 1)(x^2 \qquad - 10) = x^3 + 4x^2 - 7x - 10$

*multiply to give $x^3$*      *multiply to give $-10$*

Then find the $x$-term by <u>comparing</u> the number of $x$'s on each side. The brackets multiply out to give $-10x$ on the LHS, but there's $-7x$ on the RHS, so you need to <u>add $3x$</u>:

$(x + 1)(x^2 + 3x - 10) = x^3 + 4x^2 - 7x - 10$

*multiply to give $3x$*

Finally, <u>factorise</u> the quadratic if possible (see p18-19):

$x^3 + 4x^2 - 7x - 10 = (x + 1)(x + 5)(x - 2)$

5) Finally, if you have a cubic that equals 0, you can <u>solve</u> it by setting each bracket <u>equal to 0</u> (as you did for <u>quadratics</u>).

## I love the smell of freshly factorised cubics in the morning...

It's always a good idea to multiply out your final brackets to check that they give you the original expression.

Q1   a) Show that $(x - 3)$ is a factor of $x^3 - 5x^2 - 2x + 24$.     [1 mark]
      b) Use your answer to part a) to fully factorise $x^3 - 5x^2 - 2x + 24$.     [4 marks]
      c) Hence solve $x^3 - 5x^2 - 2x + 24 = 0$     [2 marks]

# Simultaneous Equations and Graphs

You can use <u>graphs</u> to solve <u>simultaneous equations</u> — just plot the graph of each equation, and the solutions are the points where the graphs <u>cross</u> (you can usually just read off the coordinates from the graph).

## *Plot Both Graphs and See Where They Cross*

**EXAMPLE:** Draw the graphs of $y = 2x + 4$ and $y = -1 - 3x$ and use the diagram to solve the equations simultaneously.

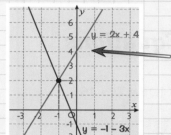

1) **DRAW BOTH GRAPHS.**

2) **LOOK FOR WHERE THE GRAPHS CROSS.**
The straight lines cross at <u>one point</u>.
Reading the <u>x- and y- values</u> of this point gives the solution $x = -1$ and $y = 2$.

 There's more on sketching straight-line graphs on p36.

If you were asked for the <u>point</u> where the graphs cross, give your answer in <u>coordinate form</u> — i.e. $(x, y)$.

**EXAMPLE:** By sketching graphs, solve the simultaneous equations $x^2 + y^2 = 16$ and $y = 2x + 1$.

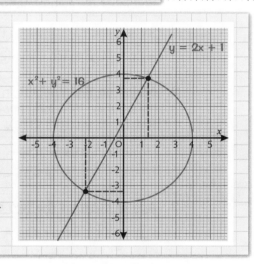

1) **DRAW BOTH GRAPHS.**
$x^2 + y^2 = 16$ is the equation of a circle with centre (O, O) and radius 4 (see p42-43). Use a pair of compasses to draw it.

2) **LOOK FOR WHERE THE GRAPHS CROSS.**
The straight line crosses the circle at <u>two points</u>. Reading the $x$ and $y$ values of these points gives the solutions $x = 1.4$, $y = 3.8$ and $x = -2.2$, $y = -3.4$ (all to 1 decimal place).

The point at which the two graphs cross is actually the <u>solution</u> you'd find if you set the two equations <u>equal to each other</u> (so in the first example, you're actually solving $2x + 4 = -1 - 3x$). This fact comes in handy for the next (trickier) example.

**EXAMPLE:** The equation $y = x^2 - 4x + 3$ is shown on the graph below. Work out the equation of the line you would need to draw to solve the equation $x^2 - 5x + 3 = O$.

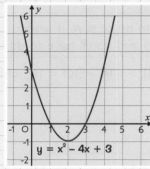

This is a bit nasty — the trick is to rearrange the given equation $x^2 - 5x + 3 = O$ so that you have $x^2 - 4x + 3$ (the graph) on one side.

$x^2 - 5x + 3 = O$
Adding $x$ to both sides:
$x^2 - 4x + 3 = x$

The sides of this equation represent the two graphs $y = x^2 - 4x + 3$ and $y = x$.

So the line needed is $y = x$.

## *What do you call a giraffe with no eyes? A graph...*
Get your graph-sketching pencils ready and have a go at these Exam Practice Questions:

Q1 By sketching the graphs, find the solutions of the simultaneous equations below.
a) $y = 2x - 3$ and $y = 6 - x$ [3 marks]  b) $x^2 + y^2 = 25$ and $y = x + 1$ [4 marks]

# Simultaneous Equations

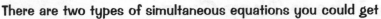

You've seen the easy way to solve simultaneous equations using graphs. Now it's time to learn the less fun algebra methods. The rules are really quite simple, but you must follow ALL the steps, in the right order, and treat them as a strict method.

There are two types of simultaneous equations you could get
— **EASY ONES** (where both equations are linear) and **TRICKY ONES** (where one's quadratic).

**1** $3x + 2y = 12$ and $10y = 7x + 16$    **2** $5x + 2y = 3$ and $y = x^2$

## **1** *Six Steps for Easy Simultaneous Equations*

**EXAMPLE:** Solve the simultaneous equations $3x + 2y = 12$ and $10y = 7x + 16$.

1. **Rearrange both equations** into the form $ax + by = c$, and label the two equations ① and ②.

   *a, b and c are numbers (which can be negative)*

   $3x + 2y = 12$ — ①
   $-7x + 10y = 16$ — ②

2. **Match up the numbers in front** (the 'coefficients') of either the x's or y's in both equations. You may need to multiply one or both equations by a suitable number. Relabel them ③ and ④.

   ① × 5:   $15x + 10y = 60$ — ③
   $-7x + 10y = 16$ — ④

3. **Add or subtract the two equations** to eliminate the terms with the same coefficient.

   ③ − ④  $22x + 0y = 44$

   *If the coefficients have the same sign (both +ve or both −ve) then subtract. If the coefficients have opposite signs (one +ve and one −ve) then add.*

4. **Solve the resulting equation.**

   $22x = 44 \Rightarrow \underline{x = 2}$

5. **Substitute the value you've found** back into equation ① and solve it.

   Sub $x = 2$ into ①:   $(3 \times 2) + 2y = 12 \Rightarrow 6 + 2y = 12 \Rightarrow 2y = 6 \Rightarrow \underline{y = 3}$

6. **Substitute both these values** into equation ② to make sure it works. If it doesn't then you've done something wrong and you'll have to do it all again.

   Sub $x$ and $y$ into ②:  $(-7 \times 2) + (10 \times 3) = -14 + 30 = 16$, which is right.
   So the solutions are:   $x = 2, y = 3$

## *Sunday morning, lemon squeezy and simultaneous linear equations...*

You need to learn the 6 steps on this page. When you think you've got them, try them out on these Exam Practice Questions.

Q1    Solve the simultaneous equations $4x + 3 = -3y$ and $2x = 9 - 5y$.    [4 marks]

Q2    Solve the simultaneous equations $\dfrac{2x-4}{2y+3} = 2$ and $\dfrac{4x-6}{y+3} = 3$.    [5 marks]

# Simultaneous Equations

## ② *Seven Steps for TRICKY Simultaneous Equations*

 **EXAMPLE:** Solve these two equations simultaneously:

$$5x + 2y = 3 \quad \text{and} \quad y = x^2$$

1. <u>Rearrange the quadratic equation</u> so that you have the non-quadratic unknown on its own (it already is in this case).  Label the two equations ① and ②.

   $5x + 2y = 3$  — ①
   $y = x^2$  — ②

2. <u>Substitute</u> the <u>quadratic expression</u> into the other equation.  You'll get another equation — label it ③.

   $5x + 2y = 3$  — ①     $\Rightarrow 5x + 2x^2 = 3$ — ③
   $y = \boxed{x^2}$  — ②

   In this example you just shove the expression for y into equation ① in place of y.

3. <u>Rearrange</u> to get a <u>quadratic equation</u>.  And guess what...  You've got to <u>solve</u> it.

   $2x^2 + 5x - 3 = 0$
   $(2x - 1)(x + 3) = 0$
   So  $2x - 1 = 0$  OR  $x + 3 = 0$
   $x = 0.5$  OR  $x = -3$

   Remember — if it won't factorise, you can either use the formula or complete the square.  Have a look at p20-22 for more details.

4. Stick the <u>first value</u> back in one of the <u>original equations</u>.

   ① $5x + 2y = 3$
   Substitute in $x = 0.5$:    $2.5 + 2y = 3$, so  $y = 0.25$

5. Stick the <u>second value</u> back in the <u>same original equation</u>.

   ① $5x + 2y = 3$
   Substitute in $x = -3$: $-15 + 2y = 3$, so  $y = 9$

6. Substitute <u>both pairs</u> of answers back into the <u>other original equation</u> to check they work.

   ② $y = x^2$
   Substitute in $x = 0.5$:    $y = (0.5)^2 = 0.25$ — jolly good.
   Substitute in $x = -3$:    $y = (-3)^2 = 9$ — smashing.

7. Write the <u>pairs of answers</u> out again, clearly, at the bottom of your working.

   The two pairs of solutions are:  $x = 0.5, y = 0.25$ and  $x = -3, y = 9$

---

## *Simultaneous pain and pleasure — it must be algebra...*

Don't make the mistake of thinking that there are 4 <u>separate</u> solutions — you end up with <u>2 pairs</u> of solutions to the simultaneous equations.  Now try these:

Q1    Solve the simultaneous equations        $2x^2 - 3 = y$  and  $7x = 1 - y$        [6 marks]

Q2    Solve the simultaneous equations        $y^2 = 2x - 4$  and  $y = x - 6$        [6 marks]

# Inequalities

Inequalities aren't <u>half as difficult as they look</u>. Once you've learned the tricks involved, most of the algebra for them is <u>identical to ordinary equations</u> (have a look back at p15 if you need a reminder).

I > All of you.

## *The Inequality Symbols*

> means '<u>Greater than</u>'     $\geq$ means '<u>Greater than or equal to</u>'
< means '<u>Less than</u>'         $\leq$ means '<u>Less than or equal to</u>'

<u>REMEMBER</u> — the one at the <u>BIG</u> end is <u>BIGGEST</u> so   $x > 4$   and   $4 < x$   both say: '<u>x is greater than 4</u>'.

## *Algebra With Inequalities*

These are pretty similar to solving <u>equations</u> — whatever you do to one side, you have to do to the other.

| <u>Adding</u> or <u>subtracting</u> doesn't change the direction of the inequality sign |
|---|

**EXAMPLE:** Solve $2x - 3 < x - 1$.

Just solve it like an equation:
$$2x - 3 < x - 1$$
(+3)      $2x < x + 2$
(−x)      $x < 2$

| <u>Multiplying</u> or <u>dividing</u> by something <u>positive</u> doesn't affect the inequality sign |
|---|

**EXAMPLE:** Solve $8x - 1 \geq 2x + 17$.

Again, solve it like an equation:
$$8x - 1 \geq 2x + 17$$
(+1)      $8x \geq 2x + 18$
(−2x)     $6x \geq 18$
(÷6)      $x \geq 3$

Dividing by 6 doesn't affect the inequality.

| <u>Multiplying</u> or <u>dividing</u> by a <u>negative</u> number <u>changes</u> the direction of the inequality sign |
|---|

**EXAMPLE:** Solve $4 - 3x \leq 16$.

Watch out for the sign changing:
$$4 - 3x \leq 16$$
(−4)      $-3x \leq 12$
(÷−3)     $x \geq -4$

The $\leq$ has turned into a $\geq$ because you divided by a <u>negative number</u>.

The reason for the sign changing direction is because it's just the same as swapping everything from one side to the other: $-3x \leq 12$ is the same as $-12 \leq 3x$, which gives $x \geq -4$.

## *Don't Divide by Variables (e.g. x or y)*

You have to be really careful when you divide by things that <u>might</u> be negative or zero — basically, don't do it.

**EXAMPLE:** Solve $36x < 6x^2$.

Start by dividing by 6 (dividing by 6 is OK because 6 is definitely positive):
$$36x < 6x^2$$
(÷6)      $6x < x^2$
(−6x)    $x^2 - 6x > 0$

It's tempting to divide both sides by $x$ now — but $x$ could be negative (or zero) so you can't do it. Subtract $6x$ from both sides instead.

See the next page for more on solving quadratic inequalities.

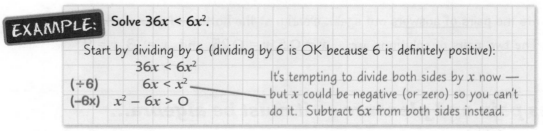

## *I saw you flip the inequality sign — how rude...*

To check you've got the inequality sign the right way round, pop in a value for $x$ and check the inequality's true.

Q1   Solve:   a) $4(x + 3) < 2(x - 1)$     [2 marks]             b) $5 - 4x \geq 15$           [2 marks]

# Inequalities

Quadratic inequalities are a bit tricky — you have to remember that there are two solutions (like for quadratic equations), so you might end up with a solution in two separate bits, or an enclosed region.

## *Take Care with Quadratic Inequalities*

If $x^2 = 4$, then $x = \underline{+2 \text{ or } -2}$. So if $x^2 > 4$, $x > 2$ or $x < -2$ and if $x^2 < 4$, $-2 < x < 2$.

**EXAMPLES:**

**1.** Solve the inequality $x^2 \leq 25$.

If $x^2 = 25$, then $x = \pm 5$.
As $x^2 \leq 25$, then $-5 \leq x \leq 5$

**2.** Solve the inequality $x^2 > 9$.

If $x^2 = 9$, then $x = \pm 3$.
As $x^2 > 9$, then $x < -3$ or $x > 3$

If the examiners are feeling particularly mean, you might get a two-step quadratic inequality to solve. It's nothing that can't be handled using the rules you've already seen though:

**EXAMPLES:**

**1.** Solve the inequality $3x^2 \geq 48$.

$(\div 3) \quad \dfrac{3x^2}{3} \geq \dfrac{48}{3}$

$x^2 \geq 16$

$x \leq -4 \text{ or } x \geq 4$

**2.** Solve the inequality $-2x^2 + 8 > 0$.

$(-8) \quad -2x^2 + 8 - 8 > 0 - 8$

$-2x^2 > -8$

$(\div -2) \quad -2x^2 \div -2 < -8 \div -2$

$x^2 < 4$

$-2 < x < 2$

You're dividing by a negative number, so flip the sign.

## *Sketch the Graph to Help You*

Worst case scenario — you have to solve a quadratic inequality such as $-x^2 + 2x + 3 > 0$. Don't panic — you can use the graph of the quadratic to help (there's more on sketching quadratic graphs on p41).

**EXAMPLE:** Solve the inequality $-x^2 + 2x + 3 > 0$.

1) Start off by setting the quadratic equal to 0 and factorising:

$-x^2 + 2x + 3 = 0$

$x^2 - 2x - 3 = 0$

$(x - 3)(x + 1) = 0$

2) Set the quadratic equal to 0 and solve it to see where it crosses the $x$-axis:

$(x - 3)(x + 1) = 0$

$(x - 3) = 0$, so $x = 3$

$(x + 1) = 0$, so $x = -1$

3) Then sketch the graph — it'll cross the $x$-axis at $-1$ and 3, and because the $x^2$ term is negative, it'll be an n-shaped curve.

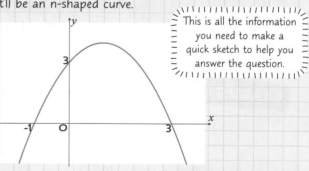

This is all the information you need to make a quick sketch to help you answer the question.

4) Now solve the inequality — you want the bit where the graph is above the $x$-axis (as it's a >). Reading off the graph, you can see that the solution is $-1 < x < 3$.

## There's too much inequality in the world — especially in Maths ...

Don't worry about drawing the graphs perfectly — all you need to know is where the graph crosses the $x$-axis and whether it's u-shaped or n-shaped so you can see which bit of the graph you want.

Q1 Solve these inequalities: a) $p^2 < 49$ [2 marks] b) $-\dfrac{1}{2}p^2 \leq -32$ [3 marks]

Q2 Write down all the integer values that satisfy the inequality $x^2 - 4x \leq 0$. [3 marks]

# Algebraic Proof

I'm not going to lie — <u>proof questions</u> can be a bit terrifying. They're usually not as bad as they seem though — you often just have to do a bit of <u>rearranging</u> to show that one thing is <u>equal</u> to another.

## Use Algebra to Show That Two Things are Equal

Before you get started, there are a few things you need to know — they'll come in very handy when you're trying to prove things.

> This can be extended to multiples of other numbers too — e.g. to prove that something is a <u>multiple of 5</u>, show that it can be written as <u>5 × something</u>.

- Any <u>even number</u> can be written as <u>2n</u> — i.e. 2 × something.
- Any <u>odd number</u> can be written as <u>2n + 1</u> — i.e. 2 × something + 1.
- <u>Consecutive numbers</u> can be written as <u>n, n + 1, n + 2</u> etc. — you can apply this to e.g. consecutive even numbers too (they'd be written as 2n, 2n + 2, 2n + 4).

In all of these statements, n is just any <u>integer</u>.

Also, adding, subtracting and multiplying integers will always give you another integer. Armed with these facts, you can tackle just about any algebraic proof question that might come up.

**EXAMPLE:** Prove that the sum of any three odd numbers is odd.

> So what you're trying to do here is show that the sum of three odd numbers can be written as (2 × something) + 1.

Take three odd numbers:
$2a + 1$, $2b + 1$ and $2c + 1$ (where a, b and c are integers)
(they don't have to be consecutive)

Add them together:
$2a + 1 + 2b + 1 + 2c + 1 = 2a + 2b + 2c + 2 + 1$

> You'll see why I've written 3 as 2 + 1 in a second.

$$= 2(a + b + c + 1) + 1$$
$$= 2n + 1 \text{ (where } n = a + b + c + 1)$$

So the sum of any three odd numbers is odd.

**EXAMPLE:** Prove that $(n + 1)^2 - (n - 5)^2 \equiv 12(n - 2)$.

Take one side of the equation and play about with it until you get the other side:

$$\text{LHS: } (n + 1)^2 - (n - 5)^2 \equiv n^2 + 2n + 1 - (n^2 - 10n + 25)$$
$$\equiv n^2 + 2n + 1 - n^2 + 10n - 25$$
$$\equiv 12n - 24$$
$$\equiv 12(n - 2) = \text{RHS} \checkmark$$

> $\equiv$ is the <u>identity symbol</u>, and means that two things are <u>identically equal</u> to each other. So $a + b \equiv b + a$ is true for <u>all values</u> of a and b (unlike an equation, which is only true for certain values).

**EXAMPLE:** A linear sequence has nth term given by the rule $4n - 1$.
A new sequence is formed by squaring each term of the linear sequence and subtracting 5. Prove that each term of the new sequence is a multiple of 4.

Find an expression for each term of the new sequence and simplify:
Linear sequence: $4n - 1$
New sequence: $(4n - 1)^2 - 5 = 16n^2 - 8n + 1 - 5$
$$= 16n^2 - 8n - 4$$
$$= 4(4n^2 - 2n - 1)$$

So each term of the new sequence is a multiple of 4.

## Prove that maths isn't fun...

Make sure you always state what *n* is — i.e. if *n* is an integer, then say so in your answer.

Q1    Prove that the sum of two consecutive odd numbers is even.    [3 marks]

Q2    Prove that $(n + 6)^2 - n(n - 3)$ is a multiple of 3, where *n* is an integer.    [3 marks]

Section Two — Algebra

# Sequences

The <u>nth term</u> of a sequence is given by an <u>expression</u> with n in, like 5n – 3.
You might have to <u>use</u> the expression to find a <u>term</u>, or <u>find</u> the expression for yourself.

## Using the Expression to Find a Term

This is dead easy — just replace each <u>n</u> in the expression with the <u>value</u> of the term you're trying to find.

**EXAMPLE:**

Find the 1st, 3rd and 10th terms of the sequence $\frac{n}{2n+1}$.

To find the <u>first</u> term, put n = 1 into the expression: $\frac{1}{2(1)+1} = \frac{1}{2+1} = \frac{1}{3}$

To find the <u>third</u> term, put n = 3 into the expression: $\frac{3}{2(3)+1} = \frac{3}{6+1} = \frac{3}{7}$

To find the <u>tenth</u> term, put n = 10 into the expression: $\frac{10}{2(10)+1} = \frac{10}{20+1} = \frac{10}{21}$

## Finding the nth Term of a Linear Sequence

These two methods work for <u>linear sequences</u> — ones with a <u>common difference</u>
(where they <u>increase</u> or <u>decrease</u> by the <u>same amount</u> each time).

**EXAMPLE:**

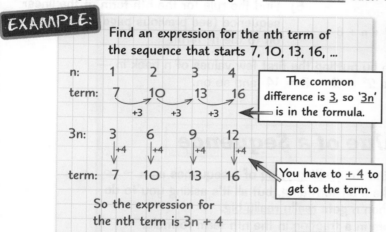

Find an expression for the nth term of
the sequence that starts 7, 10, 13, 16, ...

The common difference is <u>3</u>, so '<u>3n</u>' is in the formula.

You have to <u>+ 4</u> to get to the term.

So the expression for the nth term is 3n + 4

**Method 1 — Work it out**

1) <u>Find the common difference</u> — this tells you what to multiply n by. So here, 3 gives '3n'.
2) <u>Work out what to add or subtract</u>. So for n = 1, '3n' is 3 so add 4 to get to the term (7).
3) <u>Put both bits together</u>. So you get 3n + 4.

Always <u>check</u> your expression by putting the first few values of n back in, e.g. putting n = 1 into 3n + 4 gives 7, n = 2 gives 10, etc. which is the <u>original sequence</u> you were given — hooray!

**Method 2 — Learn the formula** The other approach is to simply <u>learn this formula</u> and stick in the values of <u>a</u> and <u>d</u> (you don't need to replace the n though):

$$\text{nth term} = dn + (a - d)$$

<u>d</u> is the <u>common difference</u> and <u>a</u> is the <u>first term</u>.

So for the example above, d = 3 and a = 7. Putting these in the formula gives:
nth term = 3n + (7 – 3) = <u>3n + 4</u>. Again, <u>check</u> it by putting in values for n.

---

### *If I've told you n times, I've told you n + 1 times — learn this page...*

Right, I've given you two methods for working out the rule, so pick your favourite out of Method 1 and Method 2 and make sure you learn it. Then have a go at these Exam Practice Questions.

Q1 Find the 5th, 16th and 30th terms of the sequence $n^2 - 6n + 2$. [2 marks]

Q2 A sequence starts 5, 9, 13, 17, ...
 a) Find an expression for the *n*th term of the sequence. [2 marks]
 b) Use your expression to find the 8th term in the sequence. [1 mark]

# Sequences

Things get a bit more tricky when you have to find an expression for a <u>quadratic sequence</u> —
you use a similar method as you do for a linear sequence, but you start off in a slightly different way.

## Finding the nth Term of a Quadratic Sequence

A <u>quadratic sequence</u> has an $n^2$ term — the <u>difference</u> between the terms <u>changes</u> as you go
through the sequence, but the <u>difference</u> between the <u>differences</u> is the <u>same</u> each time.

**EXAMPLE:**

Find an expression for the nth term of
the sequence that starts 10, 14, 20, 28...

n:     1     2     3     4
term:  10    14    20    28
       +4    +6    +8
         +2    +2

So the expression will contain an $n^2$ term.

term:      10    14    20    28
$n^2$:      1     4     9    16
term − $n^2$: 9   10    11    12

The expression for this linear sequence is n + 8

So the expression for the nth term is $n^2 + n + 8$

1) Find the <u>difference</u> between each pair of terms.

2) The difference is <u>changing</u>, so work out the difference between the <u>differences</u>.

3) <u>Divide</u> this value by <u>2</u> — this gives the coefficient of the $n^2$ term (here it's $2 \div 2 = 1$).

4) <u>Subtract</u> the $n^2$ term from each term in the sequence. This will give you a <u>linear sequence</u>.

5) Find the <u>rule</u> for the nth term of the linear sequence (see previous page) and <u>add</u> this on to the $n^2$ term.

Again, make sure you <u>check</u> your expression by putting the first few values of n back in —
so n = 1 gives $1^2 + 1 + 8 = 10$, n = 2 gives $2^2 + 2 + 8 = 14$ and so on.

## Finding the Limiting Value of a Sequence

You might get a question that asks you to find the <u>limiting value</u> of a sequence as n → ∞
(you read the arrow as '<u>tends to</u>'). This looks a bit terrifying, but all it's asking you to do
is to work out what happens to the terms when n gets <u>really really big</u>.
You'll usually only have to do this if n appears in a <u>fraction</u> in the nth term formula.

**EXAMPLE:**

Find the limiting value of the sequence $\frac{2n+5}{8n-3}$ as n → ∞.

1) What you have to do here is <u>divide</u> <u>every term</u> by the <u>highest power</u> of n (here, it's just n, but it could be $n^2$).

2) Now think about what happens as n → ∞. As n gets <u>bigger</u> and <u>bigger</u>, $\frac{5}{n}$ and $\frac{3}{n}$ get <u>smaller</u> and <u>smaller</u> (i.e. closer and closer to <u>0</u>).

$$\frac{2n+5}{8n-3} = \frac{\frac{2n}{n}+\frac{5}{n}}{\frac{8n}{n}-\frac{3}{n}} = \frac{2+\frac{5}{n}}{8-\frac{3}{n}}$$

As n → ∞, $\frac{2+\frac{5}{n}}{8-\frac{3}{n}} \to \frac{2+0}{8-0} = \frac{2}{8} = \frac{1}{4}$

## Live your life without limits — but with limiting values...

Don't let this whole 'n tends to infinity' bit confuse you — what you actually have to do is quite easy.

Q1  A quadratic sequence starts 6, 10, 18, 30. Find an expression for the nth term. [4 marks]

Q2  Find the limiting value of the sequence $\frac{3n+2}{9n-1}$ as n → ∞. [2 marks]

Section Two — Algebra

# Revision Questions for Section Two

There's no denying, Section Two is grisly grimsdike algebra — so check now how much you've learned.

- Try these questions and <u>tick off each one</u> when you <u>get it right</u>.
- When you've done <u>all the questions</u> for a topic and are <u>completely happy</u> with it, tick off the topic.

## Algebra (p9-17) ☑

1) Simplify the following: a) $(x^9)^{\frac{1}{3}}$    b) $(4x^5y^3)^2$    c) $4a^{-3}b^8 \times 5a^6b^{-2}$

2) Solve $x^{\frac{3}{4}} = 27$

3) $x^{\frac{2}{3}} = 9$ and $y^{-3} = \dfrac{8}{125}$. Find the value of xy.

4) Multiply out these brackets: a) $(3x - 2)(4x + 1)$   b) $3x(2x^2 + 4x - y)$   c) $(4x - y)^2$

5) Multiply out these brackets: a) $(x + y)(2x + 3xy - y^2)$    b) $(x + 2)(2x - 1)^2$

6) Factorise the following: a) $(p + q)^2 + (p + q)(2p + 3q)$    b) $8x^2 + 18xy + 9y^2$

7) Factorise the following: a) $5a^2 - 80b^2$    b) $4p^4 - 36q^{10}$

8) Write $\sqrt{27} + \sqrt{48} - \sqrt{75}$ in the form $a\sqrt{b}$, where a and b are integers.

9) Rationalise the denominator of $\dfrac{2 + \sqrt{3}}{3 - \sqrt{3}}$.

10) Solve these equations: a) $6(x - 4) = 5 + 2(3 - 2x)$    b) $3x^2 - 7 = 2(9 + x^2)$

11) Make p the subject of these: a) $\dfrac{2p}{p + q} = r$   b) $\dfrac{1}{p + 2} = \dfrac{5}{2q + 3}$

## Quadratics (p18-22) ☑

12) Solve the following by factorising them first: a) $x^2 + 2x - 24 = 0$    b) $5x^2 - 6x = 8$

13) Find the solutions of these equations (to 2 d.p.) using the quadratic formula:
a) $x^2 + 3x - 8 = 0$    b) $2x^2 + 9x = 6$    c) $(3x + 1)^2 = 14$

14) Find the exact solutions of these equations by completing the square:
a) $x^2 - 6x + 2 = 0$    b) $2x^2 - 10x = 15$

## Algebraic Fractions and Factorising Cubics (p23-24) ☑

15) Write $\dfrac{3}{x - 1} + \dfrac{2}{x + 3}$ as a single fraction.

16) Factorise fully $x^3 + 6x^2 - 13x - 42$.

## Simultaneous Equations (p25-27) ☑

17) Solve these simultaneous equations: $2x - y = 4$ and $x^2 + 3y = -5$

## Inequalities (p28-29) ☑

18) Solve the following inequalities: a) $x + 2 \le 4x + 11$    b) $-3x + 39 > 0$

19) Solve the following inequalities: a) $5x^2 \le 125$    b) $x^2 - 6x - 27 < 0$

## Algebraic Proof (p30) ☑

20) Prove that $(2n + 1)(2n - 1)$ is odd for any integer n.

## Sequences (p31-32) ☑

21) Find the expression for the nth term in the following sequences: a) $-2, 5, 12, 19$   b) $2, 3, 6, 11$

22) A sequence is given by the formula $\dfrac{3n + 2}{15n - 4}$.
a) Find the first, eighth and fourteenth terms of the sequence, giving each term to 3 d.p.
b) Find the limiting value of the sequence as $n \to \infty$. Give your answer as a decimal.

23) Find the limiting value of the sequence $\dfrac{4n^2 + 7}{16n^2 + 1}$ as $n \to \infty$.

# Gradients

Time to hit the slopes. Well, find them anyway...

## *Finding the Gradient*

The <u>gradient</u> of a line is a measure of its <u>slope</u>. The <u>bigger</u> the number, the <u>steeper</u> the line.

**EXAMPLE:**    Find the gradient of the straight line shown.

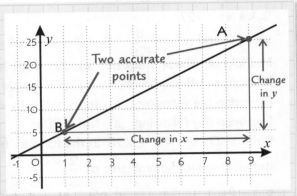

1.  Find <u>two accurate points</u> and **complete the triangle.**

    Both points should be in the upper right quadrant if possible (to keep all the numbers positive).

    Two points that can be read accurately are:

    Point A: (9, 25)        Point B: (1, 5)

2.  Find the <u>change in y</u> and the <u>change in x</u>.

    Change in $y = 25 - 5 = \underline{20}$
    Change in $x = 9 - 1 = \underline{8}$

    > Make sure you subtract the x-coordinates the <u>SAME WAY ROUND</u> as you do the y-coordinates. E.g. y-coord. of pt A − y-coord. of pt B and x-coord. of pt A − x-coord. of pt B

3.  <u>LEARN</u> this formula, and use it:

    $$\text{GRADIENT} = \frac{\text{CHANGE IN Y}}{\text{CHANGE IN X}}$$

    Gradient $= \dfrac{20}{8} = \underline{2.5}$

4.  Check the <u>sign's</u> right.    If it slopes <u>uphill</u> left → right ( ╱ ) then it's <u>positive</u>.
    If it slopes <u>downhill</u> left → right ( ╲ ) then it's <u>negative</u>.

    As the graph goes uphill, the gradient is <u>positive</u>.
    So the gradient is <u>2.5</u> (not -2.5)

    > If you subtracted the coordinates the <u>right way round</u>, the sign should be correct. If it's not, go back and <u>check</u> your working.

<u>Step 4</u> catches a lot of folks out in exams. It's easy to divide, get a nice positive number and breathe a sigh of relief. You've <u>got</u> to check that sign.

---

## *Finding gradients is often an uphill battle...*

Learn the four steps for finding a gradient then have a bash at this question. Take care — you might not be able to pick two points with nice, positive coordinates. Fun times ahoy.

Q1    Find the gradient of the line shown on the right. **[2 marks]**

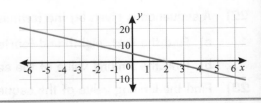

# Equation of a Straight Line

Straight line equations are often given in one of three different forms:

$$y - y_1 = m(x - x_1)$$

$$ax + by + c = 0$$

$$y = mx + c$$

REMEMBER:
'm' = gradient of the line.
'c' = 'y-intercept' (where it hits the y-axis)

You'll need to be able to rearrange your equation from one format to another, like this:

| $y - y_1 = m(x - x_1)$ | | 'y = mx + c' | | $ax + by + c = 0$ |
|---|---|---|---|---|
| $y - 3 = 2(x + 1)$ | $\rightarrow$ | $y = 2x + 5$ | $\rightarrow$ | $2x - y + 5 = 0$ |
| $y + 8 = 0.5(x - 2)$ | $\rightarrow$ | $y = 0.5x - 9$ | $\rightarrow$ | $x - 2y - 18 = 0$ |
| $y + 0.2 = 0.4(x + 3)$ | $\rightarrow$ | $y = 0.4x + 1$ | $\rightarrow$ | $2x - 5y + 5 = 0$ |

## Finding the Equation of a Line from the Graph

Finding the equation of a line by reading its __gradient__ and __y-intercept__ off the graph is nice and __easy__.

 **EXAMPLE:** Find the equation of the line on the graph in the form $y = mx + c$.

**1** Find '__m__' (gradient) and '__c__' (y-intercept).

$$'m' = \frac{\text{change in } y}{\text{change in } x} = \frac{20}{20} = 1$$

$$'c' = \underline{5}$$

**2** Use these to write the equation in the form $y = mx + c$.

$$y = x + 5$$

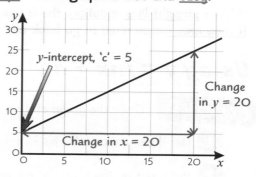

y-intercept, 'c' = 5

Change in y = 20

Change in x = 20

## Finding the Equation of a Line Through Two Points

If you're given two points, it's easiest to find the equation in the form $y - y_1 = m(x - x_1)$ and then __change it__ into the form the question is asking for.

 **EXAMPLE:** Find the equation of the straight line that passes through $(-2, 9)$ and $(3, -1)$. Give your answer in the form $y = mx + c$.

**1** Use the __two__ points to find 'm' (gradient).

$$m = \frac{\text{change in } y}{\text{change in } x} = \frac{-1 - 9}{3 - (-2)} = \frac{-10}{5} = -2$$

**2** Use __one__ of the points to write down the equation in the form $y - y_1 = m(x - x_1)$.

$m = -2$, let $(x_1, y_1) = (-2, 9)$
So $y - 9 = -2(x - (-2))$

**3** Rearrange the equation into the form $y = mx + c$.

$y - 9 = -2(x + 2)$
$y - 9 = -2x - 4$
$y = -2x + 5$

## *Remember $y = mx + c$ — it'll keep you on the straight and narrow...*

Learn both methods for finding equations, either from a graph or from two points. Then try these questions.

Q1    Line L goes through $(0, 1)$ and $(9, 16)$. Line M goes through $(21, 3)$ and $(9, -1)$.
    a) Find the equation of Line M in the form $y = mx + c$.          [3 marks]
    b) Find the equation of Line L in the form $ax + by + c = 0$          [3 marks]

# Drawing Straight-Line Graphs

You've got three methods for <u>drawing straight-line graphs</u> on this page.   Make sure you're happy with <u>all three</u>.

## The 'Table of 3 Values' Method

**EXAMPLE:**   Draw the graph of $y = -2x + 4$ for values of $x$ from $-1$ to $4$.

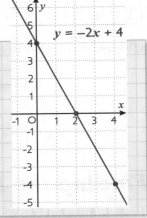

1.  <u>Draw up a table</u> with three suitable values of x.

| $x$ | O | 2 | 4 |
|---|---|---|---|
| $y$ |  |  |  |

2.  <u>Find the y-values</u> by putting each x-value into the equation:
    When   $x = 4$,     $y = -2x + 4$
                 $= (-2 × 4) + 4 = \underline{-4}$

| $x$ | O | 2 | 4 |
|---|---|---|---|
| $y$ | 4 | O | -4 |

3.  <u>Plot the points</u> and <u>draw the line</u>.

The table gives the points
(O, 4), (2, O) and (4, -4)

If it's a <u>straight-line equation</u>, the 3 points will be in a <u>dead straight line</u> with each other.
<u>If they aren't</u>, you need to go back and <u>CHECK YOUR WORKING</u>.

## Using y = mx + c

**EXAMPLE:**   Draw the graph of $4y - 2x = -4$.

**1**  Get the equation into the form $y = mx + c$.     $4y - 2x = -4 \rightarrow y = \frac{1}{2}x - 1$

**2**  Put a dot on the <u>y-axis</u> at the <u>value of c</u>.     'c' = -1, so put a dot here.

**3**  Depending on <u>m</u>, go along and up or down a certain number of units. Make another dot, then repeat this step a few times in both directions.

Go <u>2 along</u> and <u>1 up</u>
because 'm' = $+\frac{1}{2}$.
(If 'm' was –, you'd go down.)

**4**  When you have 4 or 5 dots, draw a <u>straight line</u> through them.

**5**  Finally check that the <u>gradient</u> looks right.     A gradient of $+\frac{1}{2}$ should be <u>quite gentle</u> and <u>uphill</u> left to right — which it is, so it looks OK.

## The 'x = 0, y = 0' Method

Here's a third method for drawing <u>straight lines</u>.  This one's particularly handy if you just want to do a <u>sketch</u>.

**EXAMPLE:**   Sketch the straight line $y = 3x - 5$ on the diagram.

Don't forget to label your line.

1.  <u>Set x=0</u> in the equation, and <u>find y</u> — this is where it <u>crosses the y-axis</u>.
    $y = 3x - 5$.  When  $x = O, y = -5$.

2.  <u>Set y=0</u> in the equation and <u>find x</u> — this is where it <u>crosses the x-axis</u>.
    When  $y = O$, $O = 3x - 5$. So $x = \frac{5}{3}$.

3.  Mark on the two <u>points</u> and <u>draw a line</u> passing <u>through</u> them.

*"No!" cried y "You won't cross me again" — extract from a Maths thriller...*

Learn the details of these methods.  Then you'll be ready for some Exam Practice Questions.

Q1     By rearranging the equation into the form $y = mx + c$, draw the graph of $5y + 2x = 20$.     [2 marks]

Section Three — Graphs, Functions and Calculus

# Parallel and Perpendicular Lines

You've seen how to write the <u>equation of a straight line</u>. Well, you also have to be able to write the equation of a line that's <u>parallel</u> or <u>perpendicular</u> to the straight line you're given. The fun just never ends.

## Parallel Lines Have the Same Gradient

Parallel lines all have the <u>same gradient</u>, which means their $y = mx + c$ equations all have the same values of <u>m</u>.

So the lines: $y = 2x + 3$, $y = 2x$ and $y = 2x - 4$ are all parallel.

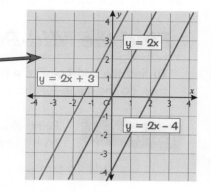

**EXAMPLE:** Line J has a gradient of <u>1.5</u>. Find the equation of Line K, which is <u>parallel</u> to Line J and passes through point (2, 9).

1) Lines J and K are <u>parallel</u> so their <u>gradients</u> are the same $\Rightarrow$ m = 1.5

2) $y = 1.5x + c$

3) $x = 2, y = 9$
$9 = (1.5 \times 2) + c \Rightarrow 9 = 3 + c$
$c = 9 - 3 = 6$

4) $y = 1.5x + 6$

1) First find the '<u>m</u>' value for Line K.

2) Substitute the value for 'm' into <u>y = mx + c</u> to give you the 'equation so far'.

3) Substitute the <u>x and y values</u> for the given point on Line K and solve for '<u>c</u>'.

4) Write out the <u>full equation</u>.

## Perpendicular Line Gradients

If the gradient of the first line is m, the gradient of the other line will be $-\dfrac{1}{m}$, because $m \times -\dfrac{1}{m} = -1$.

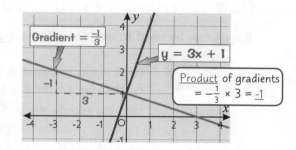

**EXAMPLE:** Lines A and B are <u>perpendicular</u> and intersect at <u>(2, 1)</u>. If Line A has the equation $\underline{4y - x - 2 = 0}$, what is the equation of Line B?

| Find '<u>m</u>' (the gradient) for Line A. | $4y - x - 2 = 0 \Rightarrow 4y = x + 2$ $\Rightarrow y = \frac{1}{4}x + \frac{1}{2}$, so $m_A = \frac{1}{4}$ |
|---|---|
| Find the 'm' value for the <u>perpendicular</u> line (Line B). | $m_B = -\frac{1}{m_A} = -1 \div \frac{1}{4} = -4$ |
| Put this into $y - y_1 = m(x - x_1)$ to give the 'equation so far'. | $y - y_1 = -4(x - x_1)$ |
| Put in the <u>x and y values</u> of the point | $y - 1 = -4(x - 2)$ |
| Write out the full equation. | $y = -4x + 9$ or $4x + y - 9 = 0$ |

*You can choose the $y = mx + c$ method or this one for parallel and for perpendicular lines.*

---

## This stuff is a way to get one over on the examiners (well –1 actually)...

So basically, use one gradient to find the other, then use the known $x$ and $y$ values to work out c.

Q1    Find the equation of the line parallel to $3x - 3y - 7 = 0$ which passes through the point (2, –1). Give your answer in the form $y = mx + c$.                    [3 marks]

Q2    Points A(1, 0), B(0, 4) and C(–4, 3) are joined together to form a triangle. By finding the gradient of each of the three sides, decide whether ABC is a right-angled triangle.    [3 marks]

# Coordinates and Ratio

Now you're all clued up on the equations of straight lines, it's time to move onto line segments.
Instead of going on forever, a line segment is the part of a line between two end points,
and there's all sorts of cool stuff you can find out about them.

## Find the Mid-Point by Finding the Average of the End Points

To find the mid-point of a line segment, just add the x-coordinates and divide by two,
then do the same for the y-coordinates.

Points A and B are given by the coordinates (7, 4) and (−1, −2) respectively.
M is the mid-point of the line segment AB. Find the coordinates of M.

Add the x-coordinate of A to the x-coordinate of B and
divide by two to find the x-coordinate of the midpoint.

Do the same with
the y-coordinates.
$$\left(\frac{7 + -1}{2}, \frac{4 + -2}{2}\right) = \left(\frac{6}{2}, \frac{2}{2}\right) = (3, 1)$$

So the mid-point of AB has coordinates (3, 1)

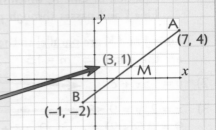

## Use Ratios to Find Coordinates

Ratios can be used to express where a point is on a line. You can use a ratio to find the coordinates of a point.

EXAMPLE:

Point A has coordinates (−3, 5) and point B has coordinates (18, 33).
Point C lies on the line segment AB, so that AC : CB = 4 : 3
Find the coordinates of C.

First find the difference between
the coordinates of A and B:

Difference in x-coordinates: 18 − −3 = 21
Difference in y-coordinates: 33 − 5 = 28

Now look at the ratio you've been given: AC : CB = 4 : 3

The ratio tells you C is $\frac{4}{7}$
of the way from A to B —
so find $\frac{4}{7}$ of each difference.

x: $\frac{4}{7} \times 21 = 12$

y: $\frac{4}{7} \times 28 = 16$

Now add these to the
coordinates of A to find C.

x-coordinate: −3 + 12 = 9
y-coordinate: 5 + 16 = 21

Coordinates of C are (9, 21)

## Make sure this page is segmented into your brain...

If you get a wordy line segments question it's often worth sketching a quick diagram to help you get your
head around the problem. Have a go at these questions to see if the stuff on this page has sunk in yet:

Q1    A (−4, −1) and B (8, −3) are points on the circumference of a circle. AB is a diameter.
      Find the coordinates of the centre of the circle                                    [2 marks]

Q2    P, Q and R lie on the straight line with equation $y − 3x = 6$,
      as shown on the right. PQ : QR = 1 : 2
      Find the equation of the line perpendicular to PQ that passes through the point R.
                                                                                          [4 marks]

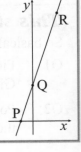

# Functions

Functions can look a bit yuck, but they're basically just equations in fancy dress.

## Functions Map Numbers from the Domain to the Range

1) The definition of a function is a <u>rule</u> that <u>maps</u> each number from a set of numbers called the <u>domain</u> to <u>exactly one number</u> of a second set of numbers called the <u>range</u>. BUT: different domain values <u>can</u> map to the <u>same value</u> in the range — see the example on the right.

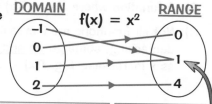

DOMAIN    $f(x) = x^2$    RANGE

2) A function is really just another way of writing an equation.

> E.g. instead of writing an <u>equation</u> like $y = 5x + 2$, you can write a <u>function</u> like $f(x) = 5x + 2$ or $f : x \rightarrow 5x + 2$. The diagram on the right shows the function $f(x) = x^2$.

| <u>Each</u> domain value maps to only <u>one</u> range value (has one arrow). | But <u>different</u> domain values can map to the <u>same number</u>. |

**EXAMPLE:** $f(x) = x + 7$ for $-1 \leq x \leq 1$   Find the range of $f(x)$.

The <u>domain</u> of the function is $-1 \leq x \leq 1$ :    $-1 \leq x \leq 1$

Add 7 all the way through the <u>inequality</u>.    $6 \leq x + 7 \leq 8$

<u>$f(x)$</u> $= x + 7$, so you're done.    $6 \leq f(x) \leq 8$

> Domains and ranges are often described with inequalities. Domains are given in terms of $x$, and ranges in terms of $f(x)$.

3) You might be given <u>x</u> and asked to find <u>f(x)</u>, or vice versa:

**EXAMPLES:**

**1.** If $f(x) = x^2 - x + 7$, find $f(3)$.

Just substitute 3 for x.
$f(x) = 3^2 - 3 + 7$
$= 9 - 3 + 7 = 13$

**2.** $f(x) = \dfrac{1 - 2x}{x + 4}$. Given that $f(x) = -\dfrac{1}{2}$, find $x$.

$\dfrac{1 - 2x}{x + 4} = -\dfrac{1}{2} \Rightarrow$

Just solve this like an ordinary equation.

$2(1 - 2x) = -1(x + 4)$
$2 - 4x = -x - 4$
$3x = 6$
$x = 2$

## Excluding Values from a Domain

Sometimes certain values <u>won't work</u> in a function. You have to <u>exclude</u> these from the domain. These <u>two rules</u> will help you decide <u>which values</u> must be excluded (if any).

1) **Dividing by zero is undefined.**   E.g. for $f(x) = \dfrac{12}{x}$ you'd have to exclude <u>$x = 0$</u>.

2) **You can't find the square root of a negative number.**   E.g. for $f(x) = \sqrt{(x - 2)}$ you'd have to exclude <u>$x < 2$</u>.

**EXAMPLE:** State which value of $x$ cannot be included in the domain of f: $x \rightarrow \dfrac{1 - 2x}{x + 4}$.

Dividing by zero is <u>undefined</u>:   $x + 4 = 0 \Rightarrow x = -4$ cannot be included.

## This page has really put the 'fun' into 'functions'...

This is another topic where practice really does make perfect. Start here with this Exam Practice Question:

Q1    $f(x) = \sqrt{\dfrac{4}{x + 3}}$      a) Solve $f(a) = 2$                             [2 marks]

        b) State the values of $x$ which cannot be included in the domain of f.        [2 marks]

Section Three — Graphs, Functions and Calculus

# Functions

There are all sorts of <u>different types</u> of functions — this page will get you clued up on some common ones.

## *Some Functions are Increasing or Decreasing*

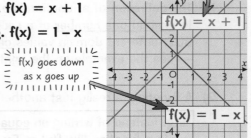

f(x) goes up as x goes up

1)  A function where f(a) ≥ f(b) when a > b is called <u>increasing</u>.  E.g. f(x) = x + 1

2)  A function where f(a) ≤ f(b) when a > b is called <u>decreasing</u>.  E.g. f(x) = 1 − x

3)  <u>Not all</u> functions are increasing or decreasing, some go <u>up and down</u> as x increases.  E.g. f(x) = x²

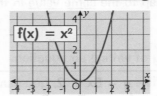

f(x) = x²

f(x) goes down as x goes up

## *Functions can be Defined with More than One Equation*

Sometimes a function can be given using <u>different equations</u> for <u>different parts</u> of the <u>domain</u>.

**EXAMPLE:**

A function g(x) is defined as
$$g(x) = 4 \qquad 0 \le x < 2$$
$$= 6 - x \qquad 2 \le x \le 4$$
$$= 3x - 10 \qquad 4 < x \le 5$$

Draw the graph of y = g(x) for 0 ≤ x ≤ 5

Draw the <u>graph</u> of the <u>equation</u> for each separate part of the domain.

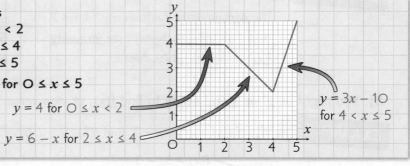

y = 4 for 0 ≤ x < 2

y = 6 − x for 2 ≤ x ≤ 4

y = 3x − 10 for 4 < x ≤ 5

You can find the <u>equations</u> for a <u>function</u> from its <u>graph</u>, just like with straight lines:

**EXAMPLE:**

y = f(x) is shown on the graph on the right, for domain −6 ≤ x ≤ 3. Work out the function f(x).

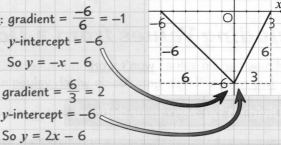

The graph of f(x) is made up of <u>two straight lines</u>.

Use <u>y = mx + c</u> to find the <u>equation</u> of each straight line.

For −6 ≤ x < 0: gradient = $\frac{-6}{6}$ = −1

y-intercept = −6

So y = −x − 6

For 0 ≤ x ≤ 3: gradient = $\frac{6}{3}$ = 2

y-intercept = −6

So y = 2x − 6

Put the equations together to give the <u>function</u>.

$$f(x) = -x - 6 \qquad -6 \le x < 0$$
$$= 2x - 6 \qquad 0 \le x \le 3$$

## *I don't know how I'd function without revision guides...*

If you have a function that's made up of lots of equations, just deal with them one at a time and you'll be fine.

Q1  f(x) = ax + b for 1 ≤ x ≤ 3, the range of f(x) is 4 ≤ f(x) ≤ 10.
f(x) is an increasing function.  Find the values of a and b.  [4 marks]

Q2  $f(x) = -x - 5 \qquad x < -2$
$= 2x + 1 \qquad -2 \le x \le 2$
$= 5 \qquad x > 2$

a)  Draw the graph of y = f(x) for −5 ≤ x ≤ 5    [3 marks]    b)  Solve f(x) = 7    [2 marks]

# Quadratic Graphs

Quadratic functions can sound pretty darn impressive — "What did you do in Maths today, dear?", "Drawing the graphs of quadratic functions and solving the resulting quadratic equation graphically." Like wow. Seriously.

## Plotting and Solving Quadratics

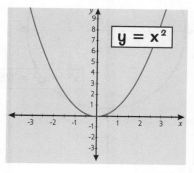

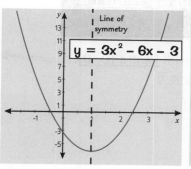

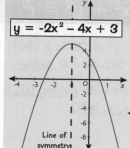

Quadratic functions are of the form y = anything with $x^2$ (but not higher powers of x).

$x^2$ graphs all have the same symmetrical bucket shape.

If the $x^2$ bit has a '−' in front of it then the bucket is upside down.

**EXAMPLE:** Complete the table of values for the equation $y = x^2 - 2x - 6$ and then draw the graph.

| x | -3 | -2 | -1 | 0 | 1 | 2 | 3 | 4 | 5 |
|---|----|----|----|----|----|----|----|----|----|
| y | 9 | 2 | -3 | -6 | -7 | -6 | -3 | 2 | 9 |

**1** Work out each y-value by substituting the corresponding x-value into the equation.

$y = (-3)^2 - (2 \times -3) - 6$
$= 9 - (-6) - 6 = 9$

$y = (4)^2 - (2 \times 4) - 6$
$= 16 - 8 - 6 = 2$

**2** Plot the points and join them with a completely smooth curve. Definitely DON'T use a ruler.

This point is obviously wrong.

NEVER EVER let one point drag your line off in some ridiculous direction. When a graph is generated from an equation, you never get spikes or lumps — only MISTAKES.

## Solving Quadratic Equations

Now celebrate the only way graphs know how: line dancing.

**EXAMPLE:** Use the graph of $y = x^2 - 2x - 6$ to solve the equation $x^2 - 2x - 6 = 0$. Give your answers to 1 d.p.

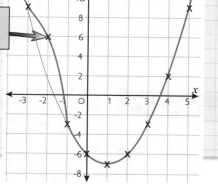

The equation $x^2 - 2x - 6 = 0$ is what you get when you put y = 0 into the graph's equation, $y = x^2 - 2x - 6$.

So to solve the equation, all you do is read the x-values where y = 0, i.e. where it crosses the x-axis.

So the solutions are x = −1.6 and x = 3.6.

Quadratic equations usually have 2 solutions.

## How refreshing — a page on graphs. Not seen one of those in a while...

You know the deal by now — learn what's on this page, then treat yourself to answering the question below.

Q1 a) Draw the graph of $y = x^2 + 3x + 2$ for values of x between −6 and 3. [4 marks]

b) Use your graph to estimate the solutions to $x^2 + 3x + 2 = 9$. [1 mark]

# Equation of a Circle

I always say a <u>beautiful shape</u> deserves a <u>beautiful formula</u>, and here you've got one of my favourite double-acts...

## *Circles Centred on (0, 0): $x^2 + y^2 = r^2$*

The equation for a circle with <u>centre (0, 0)</u> and <u>radius r</u> is:

$$x^2 + y^2 = r^2$$

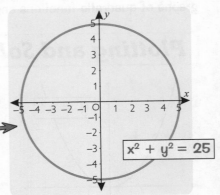

$x^2 + y^2 = 25$ is a circle with <u>centre (0, 0)</u>.
$r^2 = 25$, so the <u>radius, r, is 5</u>.

$$x^2 + y^2 = 25$$

$x^2 + y^2 = 100$ is a circle with <u>centre (0, 0)</u>.
$r^2 = 100$, so the <u>radius, r, is 10</u>.

## *Circles Centred on (a, b): $(x - a)^2 + (y - b)^2 = r^2$*

The equation of a circle <u>centred on (a, b)</u> looks complicated, but it's all based on <u>Pythagoras' theorem</u>. Take a look at the circle below, with centre (a, b) and radius r.

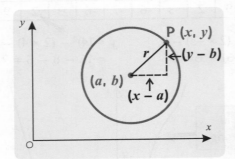

Joining a point P (x, y) on the circumference of the circle to its centre (a, b) creates a <u>right-angled triangle</u>.

Use <u>Pythagoras' theorem</u> on this triangle:

$$(x - a)^2 + (y - b)^2 = r^2$$

This is the equation for the circle. It's as easy as that.

The equation for a circle with <u>centre (a, b)</u> and <u>radius r</u> is:

$$(x - a)^2 + (y - b)^2 = r^2$$

**EXAMPLES:**

**1.** Find the centre and radius of the circle with equation $(x - 2)^2 + (y + 3)^2 = 16$

And as if by magic, here it is.

Compare $(x - 2)^2 + (y + 3)^2 = 16$ with the <u>general equation</u> for a circle with centre (a, b) and radius r:

$(x - a)^2 + (y - b)^2 = r^2$

$a = 2$, $b = -3$, $r = \sqrt{16} = 4$

Centre: $(a, b) = (2, -3)$
Radius: $r = 4$

**2.** Write down the equation of the circle with centre (−4, 2) and radius 6.

The question says, '<u>write down</u>', so you don't need to do any working — just put the <u>radius</u> and <u>centre</u> into the general equation for a circle with centre (a, b) and radius r.

$(x - a)^2 + (y - b)^2 = r^2$

$a = -4$, $b = 2$, $r = 6$

$(x + 4)^2 + (y - 2)^2 = 36$

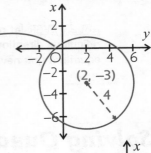

Circles can be tricky to sketch freehand. A compass is definitely the way forward.

## *Round round baby, round round like a circle baby...*

Circles are pretty straightforward really, well straightround... or roundforward? Anyway, try this question:

Q1     A circle has centre (0, 0) and passes through the point (6, 0).

     a) Write down the equation of the circle.              [1 mark]

     b) The circle is translated so that (6, 0) maps to (2, 3). Give the equation of the new circle.    [2 marks]

# Equation of a Circle

Just when you thought you knew all there was to know about <u>equations of circles</u>, along comes another page with a whole load of new stuff to learn. Ho hum, best get on with it...

## Rearrange the Equation into the Familiar Form

Sometimes you'll be given an equation for a <u>circle</u> that doesn't look much like $(x - a)^2 + (y - b)^2 = r^2$.

This is a bit of a pain, because it means you can't immediately tell what the <u>radius</u> is or where the <u>centre</u> is. But all it takes is a bit of <u>rearranging</u>:

> 1) Group the <u>x-terms</u> together and the <u>y-terms</u> together on the <u>left hand side</u>.
>
> 2) <u>Complete the square</u> for x and y.
>
> 3) Move the <u>numbers</u> left outside the brackets to the <u>right hand side</u>.

**EXAMPLE:** $x^2 + y^2 - 6x + 4y + 4 = 0$ is the equation of a circle.

a) Express the equation for the circle in the form $(x - a)^2 + (y - b)^2 = r^2$

Get all the <u>x bits</u> together and all the <u>y bits</u> together.

$$x^2 + y^2 - 6x + 4y + 4 = 0$$
$$x^2 - 6x + y^2 + 4y + 4 = 0$$

Then <u>rearrange</u> them into squared brackets — this is just like <u>completing the square</u>.

$$(x - 3)^2 - 9 + (y + 2)^2 - 4 + 4 = 0$$

Move all the leftover <u>numbers</u> to the <u>right</u> hand side.

$$(x - 3)^2 + (y + 2)^2 = 9$$

 Have a look at p21-22 for more on completing the square.

b) Draw the graph of the circle $x^2 + y^2 - 6x + 4y + 4 = 0$ on the axes given.

Use the equation from above.

This is the <u>usual form</u> → $(x - 3)^2 + (y + 2)^2 = 9$
— so you can just read off the centre and radius.

Radius $= \sqrt{9} = 3$

Centre $= (3, -2)$

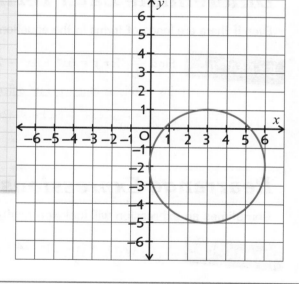

## Completing the square... to make a circle... What madness is this?

This page is really just a load of algebra, and everyone loves algebra*, so what's not to love?

Q1    Match each equation for a circle in the top row with the correct description in the bottom row.

| $x^2 + y^2 = 34$ | $x^2 + y^2 - 2x + 4y + 4 = 0$ | $x^2 + y^2 = 2(6x + 3y - 10)$ |
|---|---|---|

| Circle with centre $(1, -2)$ | Circle with diameter 8 | Circle passing through $(-5, 3)$ | Circle with radius 5 |
|---|---|---|---|

[3 marks]

* 1 out of 1 people in our survey answered 'Yes' when asked 'Don't you just love algebra?'.

**Section Three — Graphs, Functions and Calculus**

# Differentiation

This page just shows you <u>how to do</u> differentiation. <u>Why you do it</u> is covered on the next page.

## *Use the Formula to Differentiate Powers of x*

This means 'the result of differentiating the thing in the brackets'.

$$\frac{d}{dx}(x^n) = nx^{n-1}$$

If $y = x^n$, then you write:

**EXAMPLES:**

**1.** Differentiate $y$ when $y = x^5$

$n$ is just the power of $x$, so here $n = 5$

$$\frac{dy}{dx} = nx^{n-1} = 5x^4$$

**2.** Differentiate $6x^3$

Ignore the 6 and just differentiate the $x$ bit... $\qquad \frac{dy}{dx} = 6(3x^2)$

... then simplify. $\qquad = 18x^2$

**3.** Differentiate $y$ when $y = 24x$

$x = x^1$, so $n = 1$:

$$\frac{dy}{dx} = 24(1 \times x^0)$$
$$= 24$$

When you've only got an $x$-term you just end up with the <u>number in front of the $x$</u>.

**4.** Differentiate $y$ when $y = 5$

You need every term to be a <u>power of $x$</u> to differentiate. $x^0 = 1$, so use this to make 5 a power of $x$:

$$y = 5 \Rightarrow y = 5x^0$$

$$\frac{dy}{dx} = 5(0 \times x^{-1}) = 0$$

Isolated numbers just <u>disappear</u> when you differentiate.

## *Differentiate Each Term in an Equation Separately*

Even if there are loads of terms in the equation, it doesn't matter. Differentiate each bit <u>separately</u> and you'll be fine.

**EXAMPLE:** Find $\frac{dy}{dx}$ for $y = 6x^4 + 4x^3 - 2x + 1$.

Think of this as <u>four separate differentiations</u>: $\frac{dy}{dx} = 6(4x^3) + 4(3x^2) - 2 + 0 = 24x^3 + 12x^2 - 2$

i.e. $\frac{dy}{dx} = \frac{d}{dx}(6x^4) + \frac{d}{dx}(4x^3) - \frac{d}{dx}(2x) + \frac{d}{dx}(1)$

## *Rearrange Expressions so you can Differentiate*

Sometimes an expression will look too <u>nasty</u> to differentiate. Don't panic — just <u>rearrange</u> it into powers of $x$.

**EXAMPLE:** $y = \frac{(\sqrt{x})^6 + (x-2)^2 - 4}{x}$. Work out $\frac{dy}{dx}$.

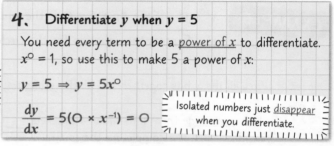

Have a look back at the algebra section if this is baffling you.

Use the <u>power rules</u> on $(\sqrt{x})^6$

Expand out $(x-2)^2$ and <u>cancel</u>.

Now you can <u>differentiate</u> as usual.

$y = \frac{(x^{\frac{1}{2}})^6 + (x-2)^2 - 4}{x} = \frac{x^3 + (x-2)^2 - 4}{x}$

$= \frac{x^3 + x^2 - 4x}{x} = x^2 + x - 4$

$\frac{dy}{dx} = 2x + 1$

---

## *Differentiate yourself from the crowd — wear your clothes backwards...*

Luckily, once you can do the simple stuff, you should be all right. Longer equations are just made up of simple little terms, so they're not really that much harder. Now try these Exam Practice Questions:

Q1 $\quad y = 3x + 2x^3 - 1$. Work out $\frac{dy}{dx}$. $\quad$ [2 marks] $\qquad$ Q2 $\quad$ Find $\frac{dy}{dx}$ for $y = x^3(3 - 5x^2)$. $\quad$ [2 marks]

# Differentiation

The gradient of a curve is <u>constantly changing</u>.
You can draw a tangent to estimate what it is at a point, but differentiation means you can find it <u>exactly</u>.

## Use Differentiation to Find a Gradient

<u>Differentiating</u> the equation of a curve gives you an <u>expression</u> for the curve's gradient.
Then you can find the gradient of the curve at any point by <u>substituting the value for x</u> into the expression.

**EXAMPLE:** Find the gradient of the graph $y = x^2$ at $x = 1$ and $x = -2$.

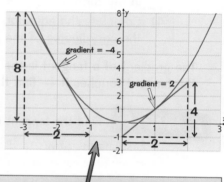

| | |
|---|---|
| <u>Differentiate</u> to get the gradient expression: | $y = x^2 \Rightarrow \dfrac{dy}{dx} = 2x$ |
| Now when <u>$x = 1$</u>, | $\dfrac{dy}{dx} = 2 \times 1 = 2$ <br> So the gradient at $x = 1$ is 2. |
| And when <u>$x = -2$</u>, | $\dfrac{dy}{dx} = 2 \times -2 = -4$ <br> So the gradient at $x = -2$ is $-4$. |

You can work out gradients by drawing <u>tangents</u> like this.
But <u>differentiation</u> is a lot quicker and more accurate.

## Differentiating Gives the Rate of Change

You can differentiate to find a <u>rate of change</u> — how fast something is decreasing or increasing compared to something else.

The '<u>rate of change of y with respect to x</u>' means how fast y is changing compared to x — it's the <u>same</u> thing as the <u>gradient</u>.

**EXAMPLE:** $y = x(2x + 5)^2$

Work out the rate of change of $y$ with respect to $x$ when $x = -1$.

| | |
|---|---|
| The '<u>rate of change</u> of $y$ with respect to $x$ when $x = -1$' is $\dfrac{dy}{dx}$ at $x = -1$. | |
| <u>Expand</u> the expression... | $y = x(2x + 5)^2 = x(4x^2 + 20x + 25) = 4x^3 + 20x^2 + 25x$ |
| ...so it's in a form you can <u>differentiate</u>. | $\dfrac{dy}{dx} = 12x^2 + 40x + 25$ |
| Then plug in $x = -1$ to find the <u>rate of change</u>. | $\dfrac{dy}{dx} = (12 \times -1^2) + (40 \times -1) + 25 = 12 - 40 + 25 = -3$ <br> Rate of change = $-3$ |

## Help me differentiation — you're my only hope...

Knowing that differentiating gives the gradient and the rate of change is more important than washing regularly — and that's important. Now try these:

Q1   Find the gradient of the graph of $y = 5x^3 - 3x^2 - 7x + 3$ when $x = 1$.   [3 marks]

Q2   $y = (x^3 - 5)^2$
Work out the rate of change of $y$ with respect to $x$ when $x = -2$.   [5 marks]

# Finding Tangents and Normals

What's a tangent? Beats me. Oh no, it's one of those thingies on a curve. Ah, yes... I remember now...

## *Tangents just Touch a Curve*

To find the <u>equation</u> of the tangent or the normal to a curve at a <u>particular point</u>:

1) <u>Differentiate</u> the function.
2) Find the gradient, <u>m</u>, of the tangent or normal.
3) <u>Write</u> the equation of the tangent or normal in the form $y - y_1 = m(x - x_1)$.
4) <u>Complete</u> the equation using the <u>coordinates</u> of the given point.

The <u>gradient</u> of a tangent is the gradient of the <u>curve</u> at the point the tangent touches it — find the gradient by <u>differentiating</u>.

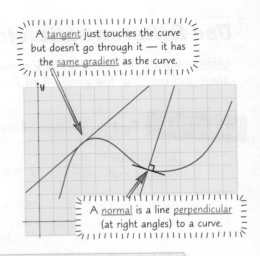

A <u>tangent</u> just touches the curve but doesn't go through it — it has the <u>same gradient</u> as the curve.

A <u>normal</u> is a line <u>perpendicular</u> (at right angles) to a curve.

**EXAMPLE:** Find the tangent to the curve $y = (4 - x)(x + 2)$ at the point (2, 8).

First find the curve's (and the tangent's) <u>gradient</u>, so write the equation in a <u>form</u> you can differentiate...
$$y = (4 - x)(x + 2) = 8 + 2x - x^2$$

...and then <u>differentiate</u> it.
$$\frac{dy}{dx} = 2 - 2x$$

The <u>gradient</u> of the tangent will be the gradient of the curve at (2, 8).
At $x = 2$, $\frac{dy}{dx} = -2$

Put $m = -2$ into $y - y_1 = m(x - x_1)$.
$$y - y_1 = -2(x - x_1)$$

Plug in the <u>point</u> (2, 8) to complete the equation:
$$y - 8 = -2(x - 2) \text{ or } y = -2x + 12$$

## *Normals are at Right Angles to a Curve*

A normal is <u>perpendicular</u> to the curve, so the <u>gradient</u> of a normal is $\dfrac{-1}{\text{gradient of the curve}}$.

Because the gradient of the <u>normal</u> multiplied by the gradient of the <u>curve</u> must be <u>−1</u>.

**EXAMPLE:** Find the normal to the curve $y = \dfrac{(x + 2)(x + 4)}{6}$ at the point (4, 8).

Write the equation of the curve in a <u>form</u> you can differentiate...
$$y = \frac{x^2 + 6x + 8}{6} = \frac{x^2}{6} + x + \frac{4}{3}$$

...and then <u>differentiate</u> it.
$$\frac{dy}{dx} = \frac{x}{3} + 1$$

Find the <u>gradient</u> of the curve at the point you're interested in — (4, 8)
At $x = 4$, $\frac{dy}{dx} = \frac{4}{3} + 1 = \frac{7}{3}$

The gradient of the <u>normal</u> is $\dfrac{-1}{\text{gradient of the curve}}$:
Gradient of normal $= -\dfrac{3}{7}$

Put $m = -\dfrac{3}{7}$ into $y - y_1 = m(x - x_1)$.
$$y - y_1 = -\frac{3}{7}(x - x_1)$$

Plug in the <u>point</u> (4, 8) to complete the equation:
$$y - 8 = -\frac{3}{7}(x - 4) \text{ or } y = -\frac{3}{7}x + \frac{68}{7}$$

## *Tangents freak me out — they're not normal...*

Tangents have the same gradient as the curve, normals are perpendicular. Simple right? Have a practice:

Q1 Work out the equation of the normal to the curve $y = x^3 + 2x^2 - 5$ at the point where $x = -2$. [5 marks]

Q2 Find the coordinates of the point where the tangent to $y = x^2 - 3x - 1$ at (4, 3) meets the $y$-axis. [5 marks]

# Stationary Points

Differentiation is how you find gradients of curves. So you can use differentiation to find where the <u>gradient</u> becomes <u>zero</u> — these are called <u>stationary points</u>.

## *Stationary Points are when the Gradient is Zero*

1) A stationary point can be a <u>maximum</u>, a <u>minimum</u> or a 'point of inflection' (where it just goes flat for a bit).

 Whatever the type, the important thing to remember is:

 > Stationary points have a gradient of <u>ZERO</u>.

2) So to find the stationary points of a graph, you need to find where: $\dfrac{dy}{dx} = 0$

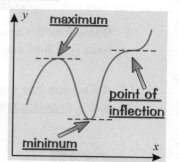

**EXAMPLE:** Find the stationary points on the curve $y = 2x^3 - 3x^2 - 12x + 5$

**1** $\dfrac{dy}{dx} = 6x^2 - 6x - 12$

**2** $6x^2 - 6x - 12 = 0 \Rightarrow x^2 - x - 2 = 0$
$\Rightarrow (x - 2)(x + 1) = 0 \Rightarrow x = 2$ or $x = -1$

**3** $x = 2 \Rightarrow y = 16 - 12 - 24 + 5 = -15$
$x = -1 \Rightarrow y = -2 - 3 + 12 + 5 = 12$
$(2, -15)$ and $(-1, 12)$

**1** First <u>differentiate</u> to find $\dfrac{dy}{dx}$

**2** Now set $\dfrac{dy}{dx}$ <u>equal to 0</u>, and solve for x.

> So there are <u>two</u> stationary points — one at $x = 2$ and one at $x = -1$

**3** Substitute the x-values into the <u>ORIGINAL</u> equation to find the <u>y-values</u> of the turning points.

## *Differentiate Again to see if it's a Maximum or a Minimum*

1) If you <u>differentiate</u> $\dfrac{dy}{dx}$ you get the second derivative, $\dfrac{d^2y}{dx^2}$.

2) $\dfrac{d^2y}{dx^2}$ is the <u>rate of change</u> of the <u>gradient</u> — it's positive when the gradient is increasing and negative when the gradient is decreasing.

3) Gradient is <u>increasing</u> through a <u>minimum</u> and <u>decreasing</u> through a <u>maximum</u>. So you can tell the type of <u>stationary point</u> from the second derivative:

> If $\dfrac{d^2y}{dx^2} > 0$ it's a <u>MINIMUM</u>.

> If $\dfrac{d^2y}{dx^2} < 0$ it's a <u>MAXIMUM</u>.

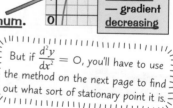

maximum — gradient decreasing

> But if $\dfrac{d^2y}{dx^2} = 0$, you'll have to use the method on the next page to find out what sort of stationary point it is.

**EXAMPLE:** The stationary points of the curve $y = f(x)$ are at $(-1, -\frac{1}{3})$ and $(3, -11)$. Given that $\dfrac{dy}{dx} = x^2 - 2x - 3$, determine the nature of each stationary point.

<u>Differentiate</u> $\dfrac{dy}{dx}$: $\qquad \dfrac{d^2y}{dx^2} = 2x - 2$

Put in the x-values of the <u>stationary points</u> to find if $\dfrac{d^2y}{dx^2}$ is <u>positive</u> or <u>negative</u>.

$x = 3 \Rightarrow \dfrac{d^2y}{dx^2} = 6 - 2 = 4 > 0$, so $(3, -11)$ is a minimum.

$x = -1 \Rightarrow \dfrac{d^2y}{dx^2} = -2 - 2 = -4 < 0$, so $(-1, -\frac{1}{3})$ is a maximum.

## *An anagram of differentiation is "Perfect Insomnia Cure"...*

There are so many uses for differentiation. Amazing. Check you get it with this lovely question:

Q1    a) Work out the coordinates of the stationary points of $y = 4x^3 - 6x^2 - 72x$    [5 marks]
       b) Determine the nature of each stationary point.    [2 marks]

# Stationary Points

Differentiation means that you can find out where a graph is <u>going up</u> and where it's <u>going down</u>. Lovely.

## *Find out if a function is Increasing or Decreasing*

You can use differentiation to work out exactly where a function is <u>increasing</u> or <u>decreasing</u> — and how quickly.

1) Some functions are <u>always</u> increasing or decreasing, some have <u>bits</u> that are increasing and bits that are decreasing.

2) A function has a <u>positive</u> gradient when it's <u>increasing</u>, and a <u>negative</u> gradient when it's <u>decreasing</u>.

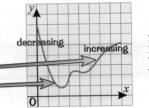

There's a bit more about increasing and decreasing functions on page 40.

**EXAMPLE:** For what values of $x$ is $y = 2x^2 + 12x - 7$ a decreasing function?

Differentiate to find the gradient.

$$\frac{dy}{dx} = 4x + 12$$

The function is <u>decreasing</u> when the gradient is <u>negative</u> — write this as an <u>inequality</u>.

$$4x + 12 < 0 \Rightarrow 4x < -12 \Rightarrow x < -3$$

## *Using Gradients to find the Type of Stationary Point*

The gradient on <u>either side</u> of a stationary point tells you which <u>type</u> of stationary point you've got.

| <u>Positive</u> on the left and <u>negative</u> on the right — it's a <u>maximum</u>. | <u>Negative</u> on the left and <u>positive</u> on the right — it's a <u>minimum</u>. | The <u>same sign</u> on both sides — it's a <u>point of inflection</u>. |

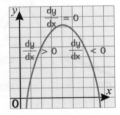 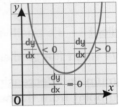 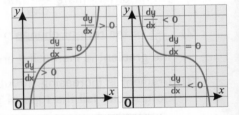

**EXAMPLE:** The curve $y = 3x^3 - 12x^2 + 16x - 7$ has a stationary point at $(\frac{4}{3}, \frac{1}{9})$.
Determine the nature of this stationary point, giving reasons for your answer.

Differentiate to find the expression for the <u>gradient</u>.

$$\frac{dy}{dx} = 9x^2 - 24x + 16$$

Sub in an <u>x-value</u> close to <u>each side</u> of the stationary point — just to the left and to the right of $x = \frac{4}{3}$.

$$x = 1 \Rightarrow \frac{dy}{dx} = 9 - 24 + 16 = 1 > 0$$

The <u>sign</u> of the gradient either side of the point tells you <u>what type</u> of stationary point it is.

$$x = 2 \Rightarrow \frac{dy}{dx} = 36 - 48 + 16 = 4 > 0$$

You could also show that the gradient is positive either side with a bit of <u>algebra</u> — $\frac{dy}{dx} = (3x - 4)^2 > 0$ when $x$ isn't $\frac{4}{3}$.

The gradient is positive either side of the stationary point, so $(\frac{4}{3}, \frac{1}{9})$ is a point of inflection.

## *This page has been a roller coaster ride — full of ups and downs...*

So if you know the sign of the gradient, then you know if the graph's going up or down. Exciting stuff.

Q1  a) Work out the coordinates of the stationary point of the curve $y = 6 - x^3$.  **[4 marks]**
    b) Explain how you know this point is a point of inflection.  **[1 mark]**

# Curve Sketching

Curve sketching is just a case of finding <u>important points</u>, then joining them up with a nice <u>smooth curve</u>.

## Find Where the Curve Crosses the Axes

The <u>points</u> where the graph meets the <u>axes</u> are the most important things to find and mark when you're making a sketch.

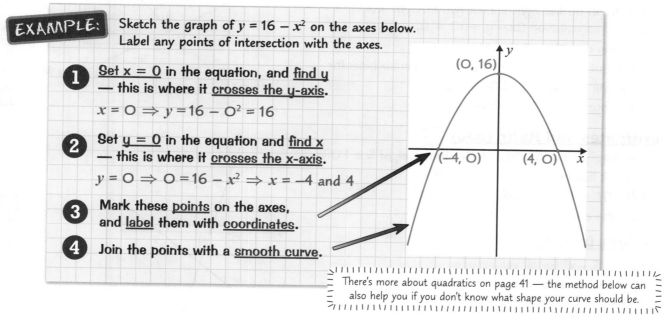

EXAMPLE: Sketch the graph of $y = 16 - x^2$ on the axes below.
Label any points of intersection with the axes.

**1** <u>Set x = 0</u> in the equation, and <u>find y</u> — this is where it <u>crosses the y-axis</u>.

$x = 0 \Rightarrow y = 16 - 0^2 = 16$

**2** Set <u>y = 0</u> in the equation and <u>find x</u> — this is where it <u>crosses the x-axis</u>.

$y = 0 \Rightarrow 0 = 16 - x^2 \Rightarrow x = -4 \text{ and } 4$

**3** Mark these <u>points</u> on the axes, and <u>label</u> them with <u>coordinates</u>.

**4** Join the points with a <u>smooth curve</u>.

There's more about quadratics on page 41 — the method below can also help you if you don't know what shape your curve should be.

## Use Stationary Points to help Sketch Graphs

You can use the <u>stationary points</u> of a function to help you <u>sketch</u> a graph.
The <u>type</u> of stationary point tells you what the graph should do <u>either side</u> of that point.

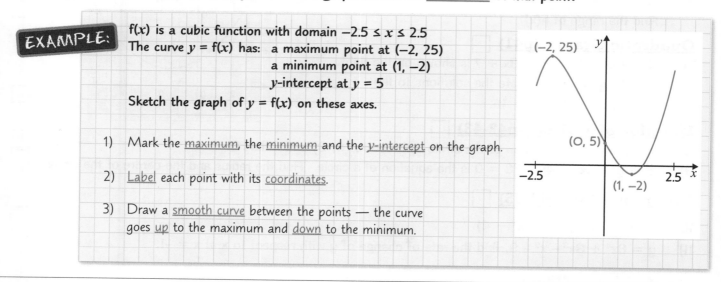

EXAMPLE: $f(x)$ is a cubic function with domain $-2.5 \leq x \leq 2.5$
The curve $y = f(x)$ has: a maximum point at $(-2, 25)$
a minimum point at $(1, -2)$
$y$-intercept at $y = 5$
Sketch the graph of $y = f(x)$ on these axes.

1) Mark the <u>maximum</u>, the <u>minimum</u> and the <u>y-intercept</u> on the graph.

2) <u>Label</u> each point with its <u>coordinates</u>.

3) Draw a <u>smooth curve</u> between the points — the curve goes <u>up</u> to the maximum and <u>down</u> to the minimum.

## Curve sketching's important — but don't take my word for it...

Curve sketching — an underrated skill, in my opinion. As Shakespeare once wrote, 'Those who can do fab sketches of graphs and stuff are likely to get pretty good grades in maths exams, no word of a lie'. Well, he probably would've done if he was into maths, anyway. Have a go at this question to see if your curve sketching is up to scratch.

Q1 Sketch the graph of $y = -2x^2 + 5x - 3$.
Show where the graph crosses the axes.

[6 marks]

# Revision Questions for Section Three

Well, that wraps up <u>Section Three</u> — time to put yourself to the test and find out <u>how much you really know</u>.

- Try these questions and <u>tick off each one</u> when you <u>get it right</u>.
- When you've done <u>all the questions</u> for a topic and are <u>completely happy</u> with it, tick off the topic.

## Gradients and Straight-Lines (p34-37) ☑

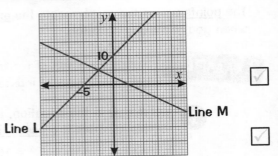

1) The graph on the right shows two straight lines.
   Line L has equation $2x - y + 10 = 0$.
   Find the equation of Line M. ☑

2) Work out the equation of the perpendicular bisector
   of points P $(-3, 2)$ and Q $(5, -2)$.
   Give your answer in the form $y = mx + c$. ☑

## Coordinates and Ratio (p38) ☑

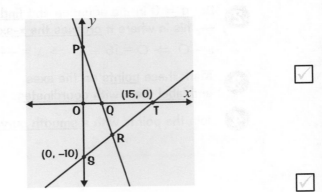

3) The diagram on the right shows the straight line PQR.
   Point R lies on the line segment TS.
   OQ : QT = 1 : 2 and SR : RT = 2 : 3
   Find the coordinates of P. ☑

## Functions (p39-40) ☑

4) $f(x) = 5 - x^2$ for all values of x.
   a) Find the value of $f(3)$.
   b) Find the range of $f(x)$.
   c) Solve $f(2x) = -95$. ☑

5) $g(x) = 2x + 3 \quad -2 \le x \le 0$
   $\quad\quad = 3 - 2x \quad\quad 0 < x \le 2$ ☑

   Draw the graph of $y = g(x)$ for $-2 \le x \le 2$.

6) $h(x) = \cos x \quad\quad 90° \le x \le 270°$ ☑
   Find the range of $h(x)$.

## Quadratic Graphs (p41) ☑

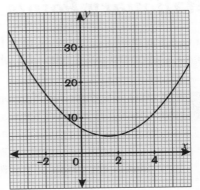

7) The graph of $y = x^2 - 3x + 7$ is shown on the right.
   Use the graph to estimate the solutions to the
   equation $x^2 - 3x + 7 = 15$. ☑

## Equation of a Circle (p42-43) ☑

8) Write down the equation of the circle with centre (0, 0) and radius 8. ☑
9) $x^2 + y^2 - 6x + 14y - 23 = 0$ is the equation of a circle. Find the radius and the centre of the circle. ☑

## Differentiation (p44-45) ☑

10) Find $\dfrac{dy}{dx}$ for $y = x^3(7x^2 + 4)$. ☑
11) $y = 6x^4 + 3x^3 - x^2 - 9$, find the rate of change of y with respect to x at $x = -1$. ☑

## Finding Tangents and Normals (p46) ☑

12) What is a normal to a curve? ☑
13) Work out the equation of the tangent to the curve $y = 4x^3 - 9x + 3$ at the point $x = -2$. ☑

## Stationary Points and Curve Sketching (p47-49) ☑

14) a) Work out the coordinates of the stationary point of the curve $y = 5x^3 - 7$.
    b) Determine the nature of this stationary point. ☑

15) a) Find the stationary points of the curve $y = 6x^3 - 8x + 3$ and determine their nature.
    b) Use part a) to sketch the graph of $y = 6x^3 - 8x + 3$. ☑

# Matrices

A lot of people think <u>matrices</u> are pretty horrific, but the maths you have to do with them is dead easy. It's just a matter of remembering to do it all in the right order...

## *Multiplying a Matrix by a Number*

To multiply a matrix by a <u>number</u>, you just multiply each individual entry in the matrix by the number.

**EXAMPLE:** Find $4\begin{pmatrix} 1 & -3 \\ 5 & 0 \end{pmatrix}$. $\quad 4\begin{pmatrix} 1 & -3 \\ 5 & 0 \end{pmatrix} = \begin{pmatrix} (4 \times 1) & (4 \times -3) \\ (4 \times 5) & (4 \times 0) \end{pmatrix} = \begin{pmatrix} 4 & -12 \\ 20 & 0 \end{pmatrix}$

## *Multiplying a Matrix by Another Matrix*

Let's say your multiplication is $\underline{A} \times \underline{B} = \underline{C}$.

1) The number of <u>columns</u> in $\underline{A}$ has to be the same as the number of <u>rows</u> in $\underline{B}$.
2) $\underline{C}$ will have the same number of <u>rows</u> as $\underline{A}$, and the same number of <u>columns</u> as $\underline{B}$.
3) If $\underline{A}$ and $\underline{B}$ are square, you can also find $\underline{B} \times \underline{A}$ — but this <u>usually isn't equal</u> to $\underline{A} \times \underline{B}$.

Here's the method to find the entries in the answer matrix $\underline{C}$:

1) Take one row of $\underline{A}$ and one column of $\underline{B}$. Multiply the <u>first entry</u> in the <u>row</u> by the <u>first entry</u> in the <u>column</u>, and the <u>second</u> entry in the row by the <u>second</u> entry in the column.
2) <u>Add</u> together the <u>products</u> from step one. The total goes in $\underline{C}$, in the <u>same row</u> as the numbers from $\underline{A}$ came from, and the <u>same column</u> as the numbers from $\underline{B}$ came from.
3) <u>Repeat</u> steps 1 and 2 till you've multiplied every column of $\underline{B}$ by every row of $\underline{A}$.

If that sounds a tad confusing, take a look at this example to see the method in action:

**EXAMPLE:** $\quad \underline{A} = \begin{pmatrix} 1 & 3 \\ 2 & 4 \end{pmatrix} \quad \underline{B} = \begin{pmatrix} 0 & 5 \\ 7 & 9 \end{pmatrix}$ Work out the matrix $\underline{AB}$.

Start with the <u>first row</u> of $\underline{A}$ and the <u>first column</u> of $\underline{B}$. Multiply the <u>first</u> entry in the <u>row</u> by the <u>first</u> entry in the <u>column</u>, and the <u>second</u> entry in the <u>row</u> by the <u>second</u> entry in the <u>column</u>.

$$\underline{AB} = \begin{pmatrix} 1 & 3 \\ 2 & 4 \end{pmatrix}\begin{pmatrix} 0 & 5 \\ 7 & 9 \end{pmatrix} = \begin{pmatrix} (1 \times 0) + (3 \times 7) & (1 \times 5) + (3 \times 9) \\ (2 \times 0) + (4 \times 7) & (2 \times 5) + (4 \times 9) \end{pmatrix} = \begin{pmatrix} 21 & 32 \\ 28 & 46 \end{pmatrix}$$

Do the <u>same</u> with the first row and the second column, and so on...

... <u>add</u> the <u>products</u> to get the entries of the answer matrix.

## *Identity* and *Zero Matrices*

Nothing to this — just two matrices you need to remember.

1) If you multiply a matrix, $\underline{A}$, by the <u>identity matrix</u>, you get $\underline{A}$. This is the $2 \times 2$ identity matrix: $\begin{pmatrix} 1 & 0 \\ 0 & 1 \end{pmatrix}$
2) The <u>zero matrix</u> is just a matrix of <u>zeros</u>. This is the $2 \times 2$ zero matrix: $\begin{pmatrix} 0 & 0 \\ 0 & 0 \end{pmatrix}$
If you <u>multiply</u> matrix $\underline{A}$ by the zero matrix, you get the zero matrix.

---

### *"Is that your arrangement of numbers?" — "No, it's my mate Rick's..."*

The best way to get the hang of following the rules of matrices and making sure the entries of your answer matrices always end up in the right place is, of course, to practise lots of questions. Start with this one:

Q1 $\quad \mathbf{X} = \begin{pmatrix} 2 & 1 \\ 0 & 2 \end{pmatrix} \quad \mathbf{Y} = \begin{pmatrix} 4 \\ 1 \end{pmatrix}$ Find the matrix $\mathbf{XY}$.  [2 marks]

# Matrix Transformations

Matrices might seem a bit weird, but they do have their uses — like in transformations.

## Matrices can Represent Points or Transformations

1) You can use a matrix to represent any point on a coordinate grid
   — the point (x, y) is represented by the matrix $\begin{pmatrix} x \\ y \end{pmatrix}$.

2) Some transformations can be represented with matrices too. If matrix A represents a point, and B is a transformation, the multiplication BA = C gives a matrix representing the transformed point.

3) The transformed point C is called the image of point A under the transformation B.

**EXAMPLE:** $R = \begin{pmatrix} 0 & -1 \\ 1 & 0 \end{pmatrix}$ gives a 90° anticlockwise rotation about the origin.

Work out the image of point P (1, 3) using the transformation matrix R.

The matrix $P = \begin{pmatrix} 1 \\ 3 \end{pmatrix}$ represents the point P (1, 3).

Multiply the matrix P by the transformation matrix R... $RP = \begin{pmatrix} 0 & -1 \\ 1 & 0 \end{pmatrix}\begin{pmatrix} 1 \\ 3 \end{pmatrix} = \begin{pmatrix} (0 \times 1) + (-1 \times 3) \\ (1 \times 1) + (0 \times 3) \end{pmatrix} = \begin{pmatrix} -3 \\ 1 \end{pmatrix}$

... to find the image of P.                 Coordinates of the image are (-3, 1).

## Use (1, 0) and (0, 1) to help you Describe the Transformation

Matrices can represent rotations, reflections and enlargements.

You can work out which transformation a matrix represents by transforming a point on the x-axis and a point on the y-axis and seeing what happens to their coordinates.

You can use any points you like — (1, 0) and (0, 1) are easiest.

> You need a point on each axis because some different transformations do the same thing to the points on one axis (e.g. rotating 90° clockwise and reflecting in $y = x$ do the same thing to points on the y-axis), and some don't move points on one axis (e.g. reflecting in the x-axis doesn't move points on the x-axis).

**EXAMPLE:** Describe fully the single transformation represented by the matrix $\begin{pmatrix} 0 & 1 \\ -1 & 0 \end{pmatrix}$.

Multiply the matrix of each point by the transformation matrix to find the transformed points.

$\begin{pmatrix} 0 & 1 \\ -1 & 0 \end{pmatrix}\begin{pmatrix} 0 \\ 1 \end{pmatrix} = \begin{pmatrix} 1 \\ 0 \end{pmatrix}$    $\begin{pmatrix} 0 & 1 \\ -1 & 0 \end{pmatrix}\begin{pmatrix} 1 \\ 0 \end{pmatrix} = \begin{pmatrix} 0 \\ -1 \end{pmatrix}$

Draw a diagram so you can see what the transformation did to the points.

Describe the transformation — make sure you give all of the information.

Rotation 90° clockwise about the origin.

> If you only transform one of these points this could look like a reflection, but when you do two you can see the rotation.

## Giving coordinates using a matrix? I don't see the point...

This stuff is basically just more multiplying matrices, not so bad eh? Have a practice with this question.

Q1  $\begin{pmatrix} -3 & 1 \\ 5 & 2 \end{pmatrix}$ maps the point (3, r) onto (-5, s). Find r and s.                 [4 marks]

# Matrix Transformations

Sometimes you'll need to <u>combine</u> two matrix transformations into one — this page will show you how.

## Combining Matrix Transformations

If a point is transformed by <u>two matrices</u>, you have to multiply them in the <u>right order</u> — the matrix for the <u>transformation</u> you do <u>first</u> always goes <u>next to</u> the one for the <u>point</u> you're transforming.

**EXAMPLE:** Point A (2, -5) is transformed by $\underline{R} = \begin{pmatrix} 0 & 1 \\ -1 & 0 \end{pmatrix}$ and then by $\underline{M} = \begin{pmatrix} -1 & 0 \\ 0 & 1 \end{pmatrix}$ to give point B. Find the coordinates of point B.

The matrices have to be multiplied in the <u>right order</u>:

(second transformation) × (first transformation) × (original point) = (new point)

So you need $\underline{MRA} = \underline{B}$ — but it doesn't matter if you do $\underline{M} \times \underline{R}$ first, or $\underline{R} \times \underline{A}$:

$$\underline{M(RA)} = \overset{M}{\begin{pmatrix} -1 & 0 \\ 0 & 1 \end{pmatrix}} \overset{R}{\begin{pmatrix} 0 & 1 \\ -1 & 0 \end{pmatrix}} \overset{A}{\begin{pmatrix} 2 \\ -5 \end{pmatrix}} = \overset{M}{\begin{pmatrix} -1 & 0 \\ 0 & 1 \end{pmatrix}} \overset{RA}{\begin{pmatrix} -5 \\ -2 \end{pmatrix}} = \begin{pmatrix} 5 \\ -2 \end{pmatrix} = \underline{B}$$

OR:

$$\underline{(MR)A} = \overset{M}{\begin{pmatrix} -1 & 0 \\ 0 & 1 \end{pmatrix}} \overset{R}{\begin{pmatrix} 0 & 1 \\ -1 & 0 \end{pmatrix}} \overset{A}{\begin{pmatrix} 2 \\ -5 \end{pmatrix}} = \overset{MR}{\begin{pmatrix} 0 & -1 \\ -1 & 0 \end{pmatrix}} \overset{A}{\begin{pmatrix} 2 \\ -5 \end{pmatrix}} = \begin{pmatrix} 5 \\ -2 \end{pmatrix} = \underline{B}$$

It's usually easier to multiply the transformation matrices together first.

The coordinates of point B are (5, −2).

To find the <u>matrix</u> that represents one transformation <u>followed</u> by another, you <u>multiply</u> the two <u>transformation matrices</u> together. The transformation that happens <u>first</u> still goes on the <u>right</u>.

**EXAMPLE:** $\begin{pmatrix} 0 & -1 \\ 1 & 0 \end{pmatrix}$ maps point P onto point Q. $\begin{pmatrix} 0 & 1 \\ 1 & 0 \end{pmatrix}$ maps point Q onto point R.

Find a single matrix that maps point P onto point R.

To map P to R you <u>first</u> map P to Q, <u>then</u> map Q to R, so the matrix that maps <u>P to Q</u> goes on the <u>right</u>. $\begin{pmatrix} 0 & 1 \\ 1 & 0 \end{pmatrix}\begin{pmatrix} 0 & -1 \\ 1 & 0 \end{pmatrix} = \begin{pmatrix} 1 & 0 \\ 0 & -1 \end{pmatrix}$

## Find the matrix that maps this page into your brain...

There's nothing to this once you remember that the transformation you do first always goes on the right — next to the point that's being transformed. Use these handy practice questions to see if it's sunk in.

Q1 $\begin{pmatrix} -1 & 0 \\ 0 & -1 \end{pmatrix}$ is the matrix representing a rotation of 180° about the origin,

$\begin{pmatrix} 1 & 0 \\ 0 & -1 \end{pmatrix}$ is the matrix representing a reflection in the $x$-axis.

Work out the matrix for a reflection in the $x$-axis followed by a rotation of 180° about the origin.

[2 marks]

Q2 The unit square is shown on the right. Draw the image of the unit square when it is transformed first by the matrix $\mathbf{A} = \begin{pmatrix} 3 & 0 \\ 0 & 3 \end{pmatrix}$, then by the matrix $\mathbf{B} = \begin{pmatrix} -1 & 0 \\ 0 & 1 \end{pmatrix}$.

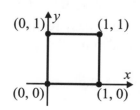

[4 marks]

# Geometry

If you know <u>all</u> these rules <u>thoroughly</u>, you'll at least have a fighting chance of working out problems with lines and angles. If you don't — you've no chance. Sorry to break it to you like that.

## 6 Simple Rules — that's all

### 1) Angles in a <u>triangle</u> add up to 180°.

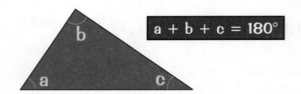

$$a + b + c = 180°$$

### 2) Angles on a <u>straight line</u> add up to 180°.

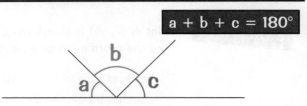

$$a + b + c = 180°$$

### 3) Angles in a <u>quadrilateral</u> add up to 360°.

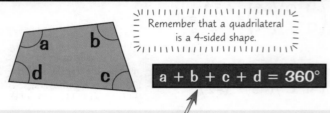

Remember that a quadrilateral is a 4-sided shape.

$$a + b + c + d = 360°$$

You can <u>see why</u> this is if you split the quadrilateral into <u>two triangles</u> along a <u>diagonal</u>. Each triangle has angles adding up to 180°, so the two together have angles adding up to 180° + 180° = 360°.

### 4) Angles <u>round a point</u> add up to 360°.

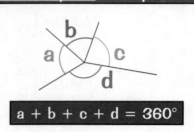

$$a + b + c + d = 360°$$

### 5) <u>Exterior angle</u> of a triangle = <u>sum</u> of <u>opposite interior angles</u>.

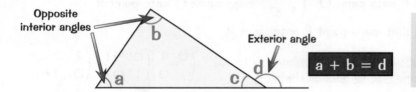

Opposite interior angles

Exterior angle

$$a + b = d$$

There's a nice easy proof of this:
a + b + c = 180° (angles in a triangle) and
c + d = 180° (angles on a straight line),
so a + b = d.

### 6) <u>Isosceles triangles</u> have <u>2 sides</u> the same and <u>2 angles</u> the same.

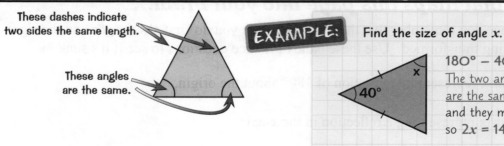

In an isosceles triangle, you only need to know <u>one angle</u> to be able to find the other two.

These dashes indicate two sides the same length.

These angles are the same.

**EXAMPLE:** Find the size of angle *x*.

180° − 40° = 140°
<u>The two angles on the right are the same</u> (they're both *x*) and they must add up to 140°, so 2*x* = 140°, which means *x* = 70°.

---

## Heaven must be missing an angle...

All the basic facts are pretty easy really, but examiners like to combine them in questions to confuse you. These angle facts are hidden in all sorts of questions, but have a go at this one as a warm-up:

Q1     Find the size of the angle marked *x*.

67°

[2 marks]

# Geometry

There are a few more <u>rules</u> you need to learn here — make sure you don't get them mixed up.

## Angles Around Parallel Lines

When a line crosses two <u>parallel lines</u>, it forms special sets of angles.

1) The two <u>bunches</u> of angles formed at the points of intersection <u>are the same</u>.

2) There are only actually <u>two different angles</u> involved (labelled a and b here), and they add up to <u>180°</u> (from rule 2 on the previous page).

3) <u>Vertically opposite angles</u> (ones opposite each other) are <u>equal</u> (in the diagram, a and a are vertically opposite, as are b and b).

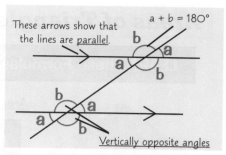

These arrows show that the lines are <u>parallel</u>.

a + b = 180°

<u>Vertically opposite angles</u>

## Alternate, Interior and Corresponding Angles

The diagram above has some <u>characteristic shapes</u> to look out for — and each shape contains a specific <u>pair of angles</u>. The angle pairs are known as <u>alternate</u>, <u>interior</u> and <u>corresponding angles</u>.

You need to spot the <u>characteristic Z, C, U and F shapes</u>:

**ALTERNATE ANGLES**

<u>Alternate</u> angles are the <u>same</u>. They are found in a <u>Z-shape</u>.

**INTERIOR ANGLES**

a + b = 180°

Interior angles are also known as <u>allied angles</u>.

<u>Interior</u> angles <u>add up to 180°</u>. They are found in a <u>C- or U-shape</u>.

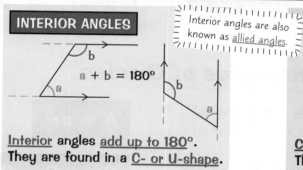

**CORRESPONDING ANGLES**

<u>Corresponding</u> angles are the <u>same</u>. They are found in an <u>F-shape</u>.

<u>Parallelograms</u> are <u>quadrilaterals</u> made from <u>two sets</u> of <u>parallel lines</u>. You can use the properties above to show that <u>opposite angles</u> in a parallelogram are <u>equal</u>, and each pair of <u>neighbouring angles</u> add up to <u>180°</u>.

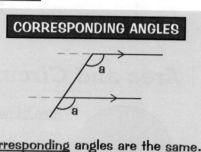

the <u>same</u>

add to <u>180°</u>

## Interior and Exterior Angles

Questions on <u>interior</u> and <u>exterior angles</u> often come up in exams — so you need to know <u>what</u> they are and <u>how to find them</u>. There are a couple of <u>formulas</u> you need to learn as well.

For <u>ANY POLYGON</u> (regular or irregular):

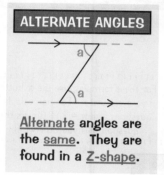

Exterior angle

Interior angle

**SUM OF EXTERIOR ANGLES = 360°**

**SUM OF INTERIOR ANGLES = (n − 2) × 180°**

(n is the number of sides)

This is because a polygon can be divided up into (n − 2) triangles, and the sum of angles in a triangle is 180°.

For <u>REGULAR POLYGONS</u> only:

**EXTERIOR ANGLE = $\dfrac{360°}{n}$**

**INTERIOR ANGLE = 180° − EXTERIOR ANGLE**

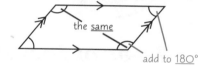

Exterior angles

Interior angles

Each sector triangle is <u>ISOSCELES</u> (see p54).

This angle is <u>always</u> the same as the <u>exterior angles</u>.

## Aim for a gold medal in the parallel lines...

Lots to remember here — and make sure you know the proper names for all these angles as well.

Q1    Find the size of the angle marked *x*.

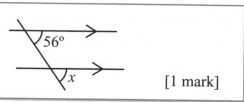

56°

*x*

[1 mark]

# Area

Here's a bit of a reminder of all the lovely <u>area formulas</u> that you need to know. By the way, I'm assuming that you know the formulas for the area of a <u>rectangle</u> ($A = l \times w$) and the area of a <u>square</u> ($A = l^2$).

## Areas *of Triangles* **and Quadrilaterals**

| LEARN these Formulas: | Note that in each case the <u>height</u> must be the <u>vertical height</u>, not the sloping height. |

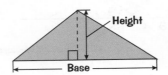

<u>Area of triangle</u> = ½ × base × vertical height

$$A = ½ \times b \times h_v$$

The alternative formula is:
<u>Area of triangle</u> = ½ ab sin C
This is covered on p64.

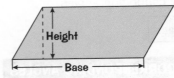

<u>Area of parallelogram</u> = base × vertical height

$$A = b \times h_v$$

<u>Area of trapezium</u> = average of parallel sides × distance between them (vertical height)

$$A = ½(a + b) \times h_v$$

## Area **and** Circumference *of Circles*

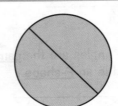

<u>Area of circle</u> = π × (radius)²
Remember that the <u>radius</u> is <u>half</u> the <u>diameter</u>.

$$A = \pi r^2$$

<u>Circumference</u> = π × diameter
= 2 × π × radius

$$C = \pi D = 2\pi r$$

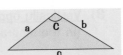
For these formulas, use the π button on your calculator. For non-calculator questions, use π ≈ 3.14 (unless the question tells you otherwise).

## Areas *of Sectors* **and Segments**

These ones are trickier — make sure you know the formulas, and what a <u>sector</u>, an <u>arc</u> and a <u>segment</u> are.

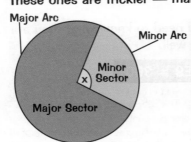

$$\text{Area of Sector} = \frac{x}{360} \times \text{Area of full Circle}$$

(Pretty obvious really, isn't it?)

$$\text{Length of Arc} = \frac{x}{360} \times \text{Circumference of full Circle}$$

(Obvious again, no?)

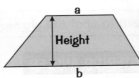

<u>FINDING THE AREA OF A SEGMENT</u> is OK if you know the formulas.

1) Find the <u>area of the sector</u> using the above formula.
2) Find the area of the triangle, then <u>subtract it</u> from the sector's area. You can do this using the '½ ab sin C' formula for the area of the triangle, which becomes: ½ r²sin x.

## *Pi r not square — pi are round. Pi are tasty...*

Oo, one more thing — if you're asked to find the perimeter of a semicircle or quarter circle, don't forget to add on the straight edges too. It's an easy mistake to make, and it'll cost you marks.

Q1    For the sector on the right, find to 2 decimal places:  a) the area    [2 marks]
                                                             b) the arc length    [2 marks]

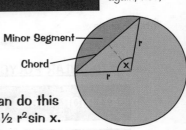

# Surface Area and Volume

It's time now to move on to the next <u>dimension</u> — yep, that's right, <u>3D shapes</u>. I can hardly contain myself.

## Surface Area

<u>SURFACE AREA</u> only applies to solid 3D objects — it's simply the <u>total area</u> of all the <u>faces</u> added together.

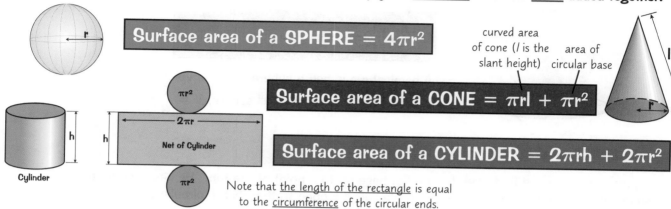

Surface area of a SPHERE = $4\pi r^2$

curved area of cone ($l$ is the slant height)  area of circular base

Surface area of a CONE = $\pi r l + \pi r^2$

Net of Cylinder

Surface area of a CYLINDER = $2\pi rh + 2\pi r^2$

Note that <u>the length of the rectangle</u> is equal to the <u>circumference</u> of the circular ends.

**EXAMPLE:** Find the exact surface area of a hemisphere with radius 4 cm.

A hemisphere is <u>half a sphere</u> — so the surface area of the <u>curved face</u> is $4\pi r^2 \div 2 = 2\pi r^2 = 2 \times \pi \times 4^2 = 32\pi$ cm$^2$.

Don't forget the area of the <u>flat face</u> though — this is just the area of a <u>circle</u> with radius 4 cm: $\pi r^2 = 16\pi$ cm$^2$.

So the <u>total surface area</u> is $32\pi + 16\pi = 48\pi$ cm$^2$.

4 cm

You're asked for the exact value, so leave your answer in terms of $\pi$.

## Volumes of Cuboids

A <u>cuboid</u> is a <u>rectangular block</u>. Finding its volume is dead easy:

Volume of Cuboid = length × width × height

$$V = L \times W \times H$$

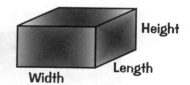

Height
Width
Length

## Volumes of Prisms and Cylinders

<u>A PRISM</u> is a solid (3D) object which is the same shape all the way through — i.e. it has a <u>CONSTANT AREA OF CROSS-SECTION</u>.

$$\text{VOLUME OF PRISM} = \text{CROSS-SECTIONAL AREA} \times \text{LENGTH}$$

$$V = A \times L$$

### Triangular Prism

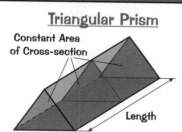

Constant Area of Cross-section

Length

### Cylinder

Using the formula to find the <u>area of a circle</u>, the formula for the volume of a <u>cylinder</u> becomes:

Constant Area of Cross-section

$$V = \pi r^2 h$$

## *Don't make it more angry — it's already a cross-section...*

Make sure you're happy with all the stuff on this page. Then have a go at this lovely Exam Practice Question:

Q1    The surface area of a cylinder with radius 9 cm is $207\pi$ cm$^2$. Find its height, $h$.      [3 marks]

# Volume

This page has a great bonus — once you've learnt it you can amaze people by calculating the volume of their ice cream cones. Who says revision isn't fun? I love it. I take exams just for kicks.

## *Volumes of Spheres*

$$\text{VOLUME OF SPHERE} = \frac{4}{3}\pi r^3$$

A <u>hemisphere</u> is half a sphere. So the volume of a hemisphere is just half the volume of a full sphere, $V = \frac{2}{3}\pi r^3$.

## *Volumes of Pyramids and Cones*

A pyramid is a shape that goes from a <u>flat base</u> up to a <u>point</u> at the top. Its base can be any shape at all. If the base is a circle then it's called a <u>cone</u> (rather than a circular pyramid).

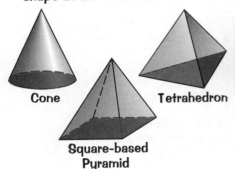

Cone

Tetrahedron

Square-based Pyramid

$$\text{VOLUME OF PYRAMID} = \frac{1}{3} \times \text{BASE AREA} \times \text{VERTICAL HEIGHT}$$

$$\text{VOLUME OF CONE} = \frac{1}{3} \times \pi r^2 \times h_v$$

Make sure you use the <u>vertical (perpendicular) height</u> in these formulas — don't get confused with the <u>slant height</u>, which you used to find the <u>surface area</u> of a cone.

## *Volumes of Frustums*

A <u>frustum of a cone</u> is what's left when the top part of a cone is cut off parallel to its circular base.

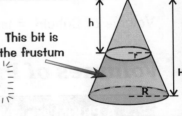

This bit is the frustum

$$\text{VOLUME OF FRUSTUM} = \text{VOLUME OF ORIGINAL CONE} - \text{VOLUME OF REMOVED CONE}$$

$$= \frac{1}{3}\pi R^2 H - \frac{1}{3}\pi r^2 h$$

The bit that's chopped off is a mini cone that's <u>similar</u> to the original cone.

**EXAMPLE:** A waste paper basket is the shape of a frustum formed by removing the top 10 cm from a cone of height 50 cm and radius 35 cm. Find the volume of the waste paper basket to 3 significant figures.

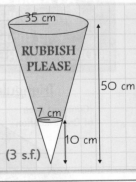

35 cm

RUBBISH PLEASE

7 cm

50 cm

10 cm

Volume of <u>original cone</u> = $\frac{1}{3}\pi R^2 H = \frac{1}{3} \times \pi \times 35^2 \times 50 = 64\,140.850...$ cm$^3$

Volume of <u>removed cone</u> = $\frac{1}{3}\pi r^2 h = \frac{1}{3} \times \pi \times 7^2 \times 10 = 513.126...$ cm$^3$

Volume of <u>frustum</u> = $64\,140.850... - 513.126... = 63\,627.723... = 63\,600$ cm$^3$ (3 s.f.)

## *No, a cone isn't 'just as good' — all the other Pharaohs will laugh...*

A common misconception is that a frustum is actually called a frustRum (I thought this until about a year ago. It blew my mind.)

Q1    A sphere has radius 6 cm, and a cone has a vertical height of 13.5 cm. Their volumes are the same. Find the radius (*r*) of the cone. [4 marks]

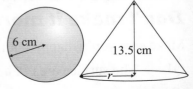

6 cm

13.5 cm

r

# Circle Geometry

It's time to plunge you into the depths of mathematical peril with a full page extravaganza on circle theorems. Sorry about that. On the upside, there is a picture of a seal, so you know — every cloud...

## 7 ~~Simple~~ Rules to Learn

### 1) A TANGENT and a RADIUS meet at 90°.

A TANGENT is a line that just touches a single point on the circumference of a circle. A tangent always makes an angle of exactly 90° with the radius it meets at this point.

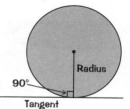

### 2) The PERPENDICULAR BISECTOR of a CHORD passes through the CENTRE of the circle.

A CHORD is any line drawn across a circle. And no matter where you draw a chord, the line that cuts it exactly in half (at 90°), will go through the centre of the circle.

### 3) The angle at the CENTRE of a circle is TWICE the angle at the CIRCUMFERENCE.

The angle subtended at the centre of a circle is EXACTLY DOUBLE the angle subtended at the circumference of the circle from the same two points (two ends of the same chord).

'Angle subtended at' is just a posh way of saying 'angle made at'.

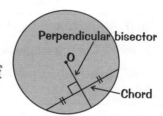

### 4) The ANGLE in a SEMICIRCLE is 90°.

A triangle drawn from the two ends of a diameter will ALWAYS make an angle of 90° where it hits the circumference of the circle, no matter where it hits.

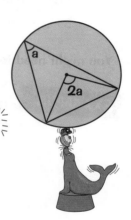

### 5) Angles in the SAME SEGMENT are EQUAL.

All triangles drawn from a chord will have the same angle where they touch the circumference. Also, the two angles on opposite sides of the chord add up to 180°.

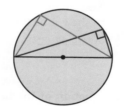

a+b = 180°

### 6) OPPOSITE ANGLES in a CYCLIC QUADRILATERAL add up to 180°.

A cyclic quadrilateral is a 4-sided shape with every corner touching the circle. Both pairs of opposite angles add up to 180°.

a + c = 180°
b + d = 180°

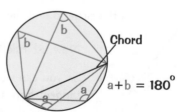

### 7) The ALTERNATE SEGMENT THEOREM.

The angle between a tangent and a chord is always equal to 'the angle in the opposite segment' (i.e. the angle made at the circumference by two lines drawn from the ends of the chord).

This is probably the hardest rule, so take care.

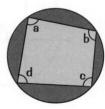
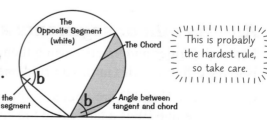

What? No Exam Practice Questions? I feel cheated.

# Circle Geometry

Now for actually using these <u>circle theorems</u> — it's often a case of having a go with any rule that you can until you find the <u>angle</u> you want. You might have to <u>use a few rules</u> to solve a problem.

## *Using the Circle Theorems*

**EXAMPLE:** A, B, C and D are points on the circumference of the circle, and O is the centre of the circle. Angle ADC = 109°. Work out the size of angles ABC and AOC.

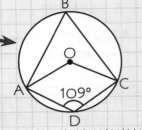

You'll probably have to use more than one rule to solve circle theorem questions — here, ABCD is a <u>cyclic quadrilateral</u> so use rule 6:

> **6) OPPOSITE ANGLES** in a **CYCLIC QUADRILATERAL** add up to **180°.**

Angles ADC and ABC are <u>opposite</u>, so **angle ABC** = 180° − 109° = 71°.

Now, angles ABC (which you've just found) and AOC both come from chord AC, so you can use rule 3:

> *Remember three-letter angle notation — angle ADC is the angle formed at D (it's always the middle letter).*

> **3) The angle at the CENTRE of a circle is TWICE the angle at the CIRCUMFERENCE.**

So angle AOC is <u>double</u> angle ABC, which means **angle AOC** = 71° × 2 = 142°.

You might need to <u>use circle theorems</u> for questions that look like they're about <u>something else</u> entirely:

**EXAMPLE:** Point A (6, 4) lies on a circle with the equation $x^2 + y^2 - 4x - 2y - 20 = 0$.

> *Circle graphs are covered on pages 42-43.*

a) **Find the centre and radius of the circle.**

<u>Rearrange</u> the equation to show it as the sum of <u>two squares</u>:

$$x^2 + y^2 - 4x - 2y - 20 = 0$$
$$x^2 - 4x + y^2 - 2y - 20 = 0$$
$$(x - 2)^2 - 4 + (y - 1)^2 - 1 - 20 = 0$$
$$(x - 2)^2 + (y - 1)^2 = 25$$

This shows the centre is (2, 1) and the radius is 5.

b) **Find the equation of the tangent to the circle at A.**

Use the <u>coordinates</u> of the centre and the point on the circle to find the <u>gradient</u> of the radius.

Gradient of radius at (6, 4) $= \dfrac{4-1}{6-2} = \dfrac{3}{4}$

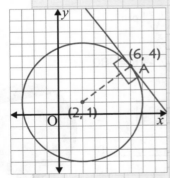

Now use rule 1:  > **1) A TANGENT and a RADIUS meet at 90°.**

So you can work out the gradient of the tangent from the gradient of the <u>radius</u> — <u>perpendicular</u> gradients multiply to give −1.

Gradient of tangent $= \dfrac{-1}{\frac{3}{4}} = -\dfrac{4}{3}$

Then <u>substitute</u> in the gradient and the coordinates of point A to $y - y_1 = m(x - x_1)$ to find the <u>equation</u> of the tangent.

$$y - 4 = -\frac{4}{3}(x - 6)$$
$$y - 4 = -\frac{4}{3}x + 8$$
$$y = -\frac{4}{3}x + 12$$

> *This is the same method as finding the tangent to a <u>curve</u> (page 46).*

---

## *All this talk of segments and tangerines is making me hungry...*

Learn <u>all 7 rules</u> and practise using them — sometimes the best approach is to try different rules until you find one that works.

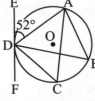

Q1  A, B, C and D are points on the circumference of the circle with centre O. The line EF is a tangent to the circle, and touches the circle at D. Angle ADE is 52°. Find the size of angles ABD and ACD.  **[2 marks]**

# Revision Questions for Section Four

There are lots of opportunities to show off your geometric skills here (reciting circle theorems is my party trick).
- Try these questions and <u>tick off each one</u> when you <u>get it right</u>.
- When you've done <u>all the questions</u> for a topic and are <u>completely happy</u> with it, tick off the topic.

## Matrices and Matrix Transformations (p51-53) ☑

1) Work out $-2\begin{pmatrix} 4 & 9 \\ 1 & -5 \end{pmatrix}$. ☑

2) $\underline{A} = \begin{pmatrix} 3 & -1 \\ 0 & 4 \end{pmatrix}$  $\underline{B} = \begin{pmatrix} 2 & 2 \\ -3 & 5 \end{pmatrix}$ Find $\underline{AB}$. ☑

3) Describe fully the single transformation represented by the matrix $\begin{pmatrix} 0 & 1 \\ 1 & 0 \end{pmatrix}$. ☑

4) Matrix $\underline{U} = \begin{pmatrix} 3 & 3 \\ 0 & -3 \end{pmatrix}$ maps point L to point M, matrix $\underline{V} = \begin{pmatrix} 1 & 4 \\ 2 & 2 \end{pmatrix}$ maps point M to point N (15, 12). ☑
Find the coordinates of point L.

## Geometry (p54-55) ☑

5) What do angles in a quadrilateral add up to? ☑
6) Find the missing angles in the diagrams below. ☑

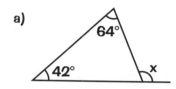
a)

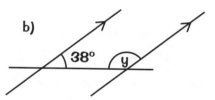
b)

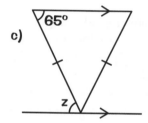
c)

7) Find the exterior angle of a regular pentagon. ☑

## Area, Surface Area and Volume (p56-58) ☐

8) A circle has diameter 12 mm. Find its exact circumference and area. ☑
9) Find the radius of the sector with area 93 cm² and angle 35° to 2 d.p. ☑
10) The shape on the right is made from a cylinder and a hemisphere. ☑
Find its exact volume.
11) Find the surface area of this solid (to 1 d.p.):

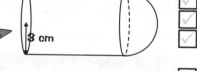

12) A sphere holds the same volume of water as 6 cylinders, each of height 18 m and radius 3 m. ☑
Find the radius of the sphere.

## Circle Geometry (p59-60) ☑

13) What is the sum of opposite angles in a cyclic quadrilateral? ☑
14) Find the size of the angle marked x in the diagram on the right. ☑
15) In the diagram below AB is the tangent to the circle at F. ☑

CE is parallel to AB.

Find the angle CDE.

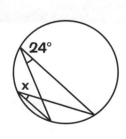

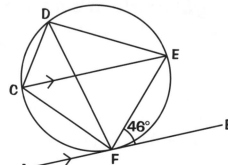

# Pythagoras' Theorem

Pythagoras' theorem only works for right-angled triangles. It sounds hard but it's actually <u>dead simple</u>.

## *Pythagoras' Theorem — $a^2 + b^2 = c^2$*

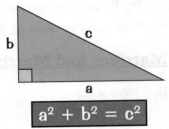

$$a^2 + b^2 = c^2$$

1) Pythagoras uses <u>two sides</u> to find the <u>third side</u>.
2) The <u>BASIC FORMULA</u> for Pythagoras is $a^2 + b^2 = c^2$
3) Make sure you get the numbers in the <u>RIGHT PLACE</u>. c is the <u>longest side</u> (called the hypotenuse) and it's always <u>opposite</u> the right angle.

**EXAMPLE:** ABC is a right-angled triangle. AB = 11 m and AC = 7 m. Find the exact length of BC.

*It's not always c you need to find — loads of people go wrong here.*

1) Write down the <u>formula</u>, then put in the <u>numbers</u>.    $a^2 + b^2 = c^2$
   $BC^2 + 7^2 = 11^2$
2) <u>Rearrange</u> the equation.    $BC^2 = 11^2 - 7^2 = 121 - 49 = 72$    *Remember to check the answer's <u>sensible</u>.*
3) Take <u>square roots</u> to find BC.    $BC = \sqrt{72} = \sqrt{36 \times 2} = 6\sqrt{2}$ m
4) <u>'Exact length'</u> means you should give your answer as a <u>surd</u> — <u>simplified</u> if possible.

4) Some right-angled triangles have three sides whose lengths are <u>all integers</u> — these groups of three numbers are called <u>Pythagorean triples</u>. For example:

| 3, 4, 5 | 5, 12, 13 | 8, 15, 17 | 7, 24, 25 |

5) You should be able to <u>recognise</u> these <u>without</u> needing to use Pythagoras' formula.
6) <u>Multiples</u> of the Pythagorean triples also make right-angled triangles, so look out for these too, e.g.:

| 6, 8, 10 | 15, 36, 39 | 32, 60, 68 | 42, 144, 150 |

## Use Pythagoras to find the Distance Between Points

Pythagoras lets you find the straight-line <u>distance</u> between <u>two points</u> on a <u>graph</u>.

1) Draw a <u>sketch</u> to show the <u>right-angled triangle</u>.
2) Find the <u>lengths of the shorter sides</u> of the triangle.
3) <u>Use Pythagoras</u> to find the <u>length of the hypotenuse</u>. (That's your answer.)

**EXAMPLE:** Point P has coordinates (–4, 3) and point Q has coordinates (11, 11). Find the length of the line PQ.

①

② Length of <u>side a</u> = 11 – 3 = 8

Length of <u>side b</u> = 11 – –4 = 15

③ You'll recognise that this is the Pythagorean triple 8, 15, 17, so c = 17

## *Remember, if it's not a right angle, it's a wrong angle...*

Once you've learned all the Pythagoras facts on this page, try these Exam Practice Questions.

Q1    Find the length of AC correct to 1 decimal place.

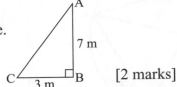

[2 marks]

Q2    Find the exact length of BC.

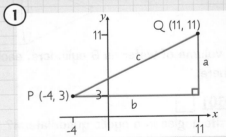

[2 marks]

Q3    Point A has coordinates (1, -2) and point B has coordinates (7, 3). Find the exact length of the line AB.

[2 marks]

# Trigonometry — Sin, Cos, Tan

Trigonometry — it's a big scary word. But it's not a big scary topic. An <u>important</u> topic, yes. An <u>always cropping up</u> topic, definitely. But scary? Pur-lease. Takes more than a triangle to scare me. Read on...

## The 3 Trigonometry Formulas

There are three basic <u>trig formulas</u> — each one links <u>two sides and an angle</u> of a <u>right-angled triangle</u>.

$$\text{Sin } x = \frac{\text{Opposite}}{\text{Hypotenuse}}$$

$$\text{Cos } x = \frac{\text{Adjacent}}{\text{Hypotenuse}}$$

$$\text{Tan } x = \frac{\text{Opposite}}{\text{Adjacent}}$$

Use SOH CAH TOA to help you remember which trig functions go with which sides.

• The <u>Hypotenuse</u> is the <u>LONGEST SIDE</u>.

• The <u>Opposite</u> is the side <u>OPPOSITE</u> the angle <u>being used</u> ($x$).

• The <u>Adjacent</u> is the (other) side <u>NEXT TO</u> the angle <u>being used</u>.

1) Whenever you come across a trig question, work out which <u>two sides</u> of the triangle are involved in that question — then <u>pick the formula</u> that involves those sides.

2) <u>To find the angle — use the inverse</u>, i.e. press SHIFT or 2ndF, followed by <u>sin</u>, <u>cos</u> or <u>tan</u> (and make sure your calculator is in DEG mode) — your calculator will display <u>sin⁻¹</u>, <u>cos⁻¹</u> or <u>tan⁻¹</u>.

3) Remember, you can only use these formulas on <u>right-angled triangles</u> — you may have to add lines to the diagram to create one.

**EXAMPLE:**

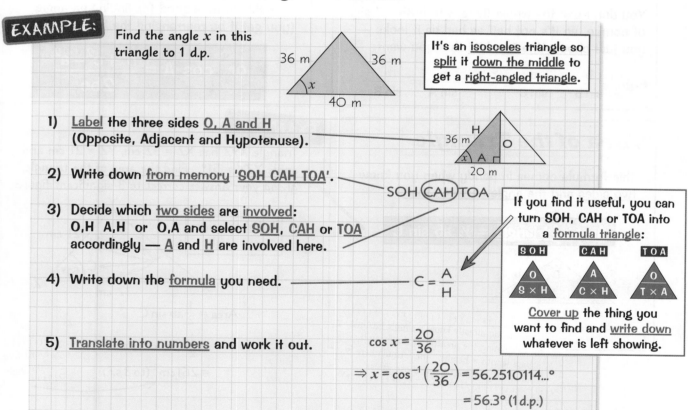

**SOH CAH TOA — the not-so-secret formula for success...**

You need to know this stuff off by heart — so go over this page a few times until you've got those formulas firmly lodged and all ready to reel off in the exam. All set? Time for some questions...

Q1   A ladder is leaning against a vertical wall. It is at an angle of 74° to the horizontal ground.
The base of the ladder is on the ground 0.9 m away from the wall.

How long is the ladder? Give your answer to 3 s.f.                    [3 marks]

# The Sine and Cosine Rules

Normal trigonometry using SOH CAH TOA etc. can only be applied to <u>right-angled</u> triangles. Which leaves us with the question of what to do with other-angled triangles. Step forward the <u>Sine and Cosine Rules</u>...

## *Labelling the Triangle*

This is very important. You must label the sides and angles properly so that the letters for the sides and angles correspond with each other. Use <u>lower case letters</u> for the <u>sides</u> and <u>capitals</u> for the <u>angles</u>.

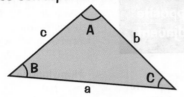

Remember, <u>side 'a' is opposite angle A</u> etc.

It doesn't matter which sides you decide to call a, b, and c, just as long as the angles are then labelled properly.

## *Three Formulas to Learn:*

### *The Sine Rule*

$$\frac{a}{\sin A} = \frac{b}{\sin B} = \frac{c}{\sin C}$$

You don't use the whole thing with both '=' signs of course, so it's not half as bad as it looks — you just <u>choose the two bits</u> that you want:

e.g. $\dfrac{b}{\sin B} = \dfrac{c}{\sin C}$ or $\dfrac{a}{\sin A} = \dfrac{b}{\sin B}$

### *The Cosine Rule*

The 'normal' form is...

$$a^2 = b^2 + c^2 - 2bc \cos A$$

...or this form is good for finding an angle (you get it by rearranging the 'normal' version):

$$\text{or} \quad \cos A = \frac{b^2 + c^2 - a^2}{2bc}$$

### *Area of the Triangle*

This formula comes in handy when you know <u>two sides</u> and the <u>angle between them</u>:

$$\boxed{\text{Area of triangle} = \tfrac{1}{2} ab \sin C}$$

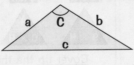

*Of course, you already know a <u>simple formula</u> for calculating the area using the formula ½ × base length × height. The formula here is for when you don't know those values.*

**EXAMPLE:**

Triangle XYZ has XZ = 32 cm, YZ = 21 cm and angle XZY = 51°. Find the area of the triangle, giving your answer correct to 3 significant figures.

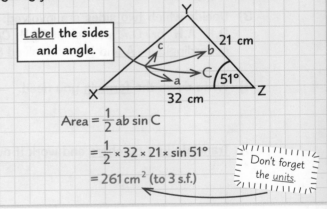

<u>Label</u> the sides and angle.

Area $= \dfrac{1}{2} ab \sin C$

$= \dfrac{1}{2} \times 32 \times 21 \times \sin 51°$

$= 261 \text{ cm}^2$ (to 3 s.f.)

*Don't forget the <u>units</u>.*

## *...and step back again. Hope you enjoyed a moment in the spotlight...*

You need to practise using these formulas — so here's an area question to have a go at, and fear not, you'll get your chance to tackle some sine and cosine rule problems on the next page...

Q1    Triangle PQR has PQ = 10 cm, QR = 19 cm and angle PQR = 24°. Find its area, giving your answer correct to 3 significant figures.

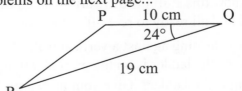

[2 marks]

Section Five — Pythagoras and Trigonometry

# The Sine and Cosine Rules

Amazingly, there are only __FOUR__ question types where the <u>sine</u> and <u>cosine</u> rules would be applied.  So learn the exact details of these four examples and you'll be laughing.  WARNING: if you laugh too much people will think you're crazy.

## *The Four Examples*

__1__ | __TWO ANGLES__ given plus __ANY SIDE__ — __SINE RULE__ needed.

Find the length of AB for the triangle below.

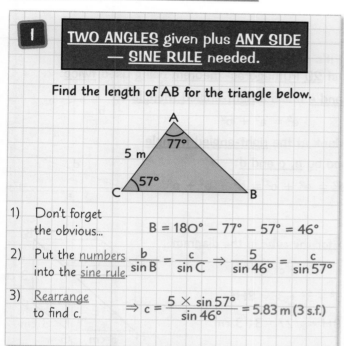

1) Don't forget the obvious...

$B = 180° − 77° − 57° = 46°$

2) Put the <u>numbers</u> into the <u>sine rule</u>. $\dfrac{b}{\sin B} = \dfrac{c}{\sin C} \Rightarrow \dfrac{5}{\sin 46°} = \dfrac{c}{\sin 57°}$

3) <u>Rearrange</u> to find c. $\Rightarrow c = \dfrac{5 \times \sin 57°}{\sin 46°} = 5.83\,\text{m (3 s.f.)}$

__2__ | __TWO SIDES__ given plus an __ANGLE NOT ENCLOSED__ by them — __SINE RULE__ needed.

Find angle ABC for the triangle shown below.

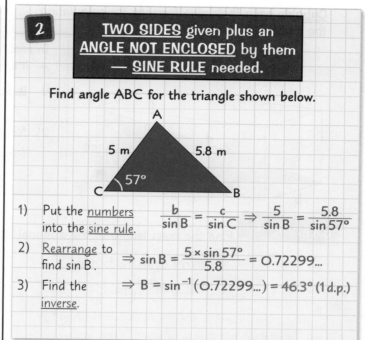

1) Put the <u>numbers</u> into the <u>sine rule</u>. $\dfrac{b}{\sin B} = \dfrac{c}{\sin C} \Rightarrow \dfrac{5}{\sin B} = \dfrac{5.8}{\sin 57°}$

2) <u>Rearrange</u> to find sin B. $\Rightarrow \sin B = \dfrac{5 \times \sin 57°}{5.8} = 0.72299...$

3) Find the <u>inverse</u>. $\Rightarrow B = \sin^{-1}(0.72299...) = 46.3° \,(1\,\text{d.p.})$

__3__ | __TWO SIDES__ given plus the __ANGLE ENCLOSED__ by them — __COSINE RULE__ needed.

Find the length CB for the triangle shown below.

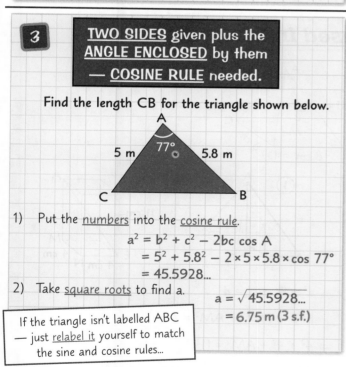

1) Put the <u>numbers</u> into the <u>cosine rule</u>.

$a^2 = b^2 + c^2 − 2bc \cos A$
$= 5^2 + 5.8^2 − 2 \times 5 \times 5.8 \times \cos 77°$
$= 45.5928...$

2) Take <u>square roots</u> to find a.

$a = \sqrt{45.5928...}$
$= 6.75\,\text{m (3 s.f.)}$

If the triangle isn't labelled ABC — just <u>relabel it</u> yourself to match the sine and cosine rules...

__4__ | __ALL THREE SIDES__ given but __NO ANGLES__ — __COSINE RULE__ needed.

Find angle CAB for the triangle shown.

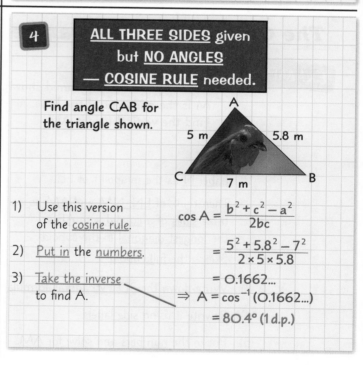

1) Use this version of the <u>cosine rule</u>. $\cos A = \dfrac{b^2 + c^2 − a^2}{2bc}$

2) <u>Put in</u> the <u>numbers</u>. $= \dfrac{5^2 + 5.8^2 − 7^2}{2 \times 5 \times 5.8}$

3) <u>Take the inverse</u> to find A.
$= 0.1662...$
$\Rightarrow A = \cos^{-1}(0.1662...)$
$= 80.4° \,(1\,\text{d.p.})$

## *4 examples + 3 formulas + 2 rules = 1 trigonometric genius...*

You need to get really good at spotting which of the four methods to use, so try these practice questions.

Q1   Find the size of angle ACB for the triangle below.

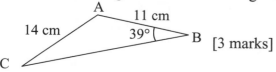

[3 marks]

Q2   Find the length of side DE for triangle DEF.

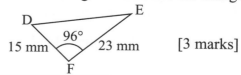

[3 marks]

# 3D Pythagoras

This is a 3D version of the 2D Pythagoras' theorem you saw on page 62.
There's just <u>one simple formula</u> — learn it and the world's your oyster...

## 3D Pythagoras for Cuboids — $a^2 + b^2 + c^2 = d^2$

<u>Cuboids</u> have their own formula for calculating
the length of their <u>longest diagonal</u>:

$$a^2 + b^2 + c^2 = d^2$$

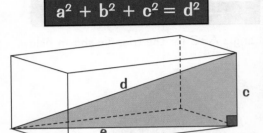

In reality it's nothing you haven't seen before
— it's just <u>2D Pythagoras' theorem</u> being used <u>twice</u>:

1) <u>a, b and e</u> make a <u>right-angled triangle</u> so
$$e^2 = a^2 + b^2$$

2) Now look at the <u>right-angled triangle</u>
formed by <u>e, c and d</u>:
$$d^2 = e^2 + c^2 = a^2 + b^2 + c^2$$

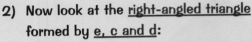
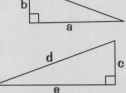

**EXAMPLE:** Find the exact length of the diagonal BH for the cube in the diagram.

1) Write down the <u>formula</u>.  $a^2 + b^2 + c^2 = d^2$

2) Put in the <u>numbers</u>.  $3^2 + 3^2 + 3^2 = BH^2$

3) Take the <u>square root</u> to find BH.  $\Rightarrow BH = \sqrt{27} = 3\sqrt{3}$ cm

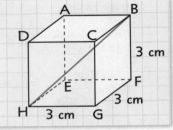

## The Cuboid Formula can be used in Other 3D Shapes

**EXAMPLE:**

In the square-based pyramid shown,
M is the midpoint of the base.
Find the vertical height AM.

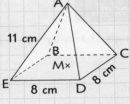

1) <u>Label N</u> as the midpoint of ED.
Then think of <u>EN, NM and AM</u> as
three <u>sides</u> of a <u>cuboid</u>, and <u>AE</u> as
the <u>longest diagonal</u> in the cuboid.

2) Sketch the <u>full cuboid</u>.

3) Write down the <u>3D Pythagoras formula</u>.  $a^2 + b^2 + c^2 = d^2$

4) <u>Rewrite</u> it using <u>side labels</u>.  $EN^2 + NM^2 + AM^2 = AE^2$

5) Put in the <u>numbers</u> and <u>solve for AM</u>.  $\Rightarrow 4^2 + 4^2 + AM^2 = 11^2$

$\Rightarrow AM = \sqrt{121 - 2 \times 16} = 9.43$ cm (3 s.f.)

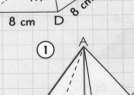
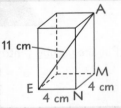

## *Wow — just what can't right-angled triangles do?...*

You need to be ready to tackle 3D questions in the exam,
so have a go at this Exam Practice Question.

Q1    Find the length BG in the cuboid shown to 3 s.f.

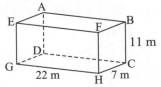

[3 marks]

Section Five — Pythagoras and Trigonometry

# 3D Trigonometry

3D trig may sound tricky, and in many ways it is... but it's actually just using the <u>same old rules</u>.

## Angle Between Line and Plane — Use a Diagram

### Learn the 3-Step Method

1) Make a <u>right-angled triangle</u> between the line and the plane.

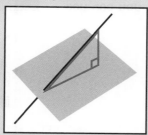

2) Draw a <u>simple 2D sketch</u> of this triangle and mark on the lengths of two sides (you might have to use <u>Pythagoras</u> to find one).

3) Use <u>trig</u> to find the angle.

You can find the angle between <u>two planes</u> in the same way — but make the right-angled triangle <u>between</u> the two planes.

### EXAMPLE:

ABCDE is a square-based pyramid with M as the midpoint of its base. Find the angle the edge AE makes with the base.

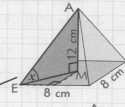

1) Draw a <u>right-angled triangle</u> using <u>AE</u>, the <u>base</u> and <u>a line between the two</u> (here it's the vertical height).

Label the <u>angle</u> you need to find.

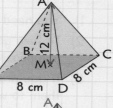

2) Now sketch this triangle in 2D and <u>label</u> it.

Use <u>Pythagoras</u> (on the <u>base</u> triangle) to <u>find EM</u>.

$EM^2 = 4^2 + 4^2 = 32$
$\Rightarrow EM = \sqrt{32}$ cm

3) Finally, use <u>trigonometry</u> to find <u>x</u> — you know the <u>opposite</u> and <u>adjacent</u> sides so use <u>tan</u>.

$\tan x = \dfrac{12}{\sqrt{32}} = 2.1213...$
$x = \tan^{-1}(2.1213...)$
$= 64.8°$ (1 d.p.)

## The Sine Rule and Cosine Rule can also be used in 3D

For <u>triangles</u> inside 3D shapes that <u>aren't right-angled</u> you can use the <u>sine and cosine rules</u>.

### EXAMPLE:

Find the size of angle AEH in the cuboid shown below.

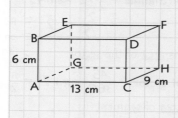

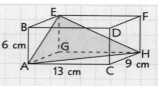 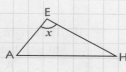

1) <u>Draw the triangle</u> AEH and label angle AEH as $x$.

2) Use <u>Pythagoras' theorem</u> to find the lengths of <u>AE, AH and EH</u>.

$AH^2 = 13^2 + 9^2 = 250 \Rightarrow AH = \sqrt{250}$
$AE^2 = 6^2 + 9^2 = 117 \Rightarrow AE = \sqrt{117}$
$EH^2 = 6^2 + 13^2 = 205 \Rightarrow EH = \sqrt{205}$

3) <u>Find $x$</u> using the <u>cosine rule</u>:
<u>Put in</u> the <u>numbers</u>.
<u>Rearrange</u> and take the <u>inverse</u> to find $x$.

$AH^2 = AE^2 + EH^2 - 2 \times AE \times EH \times \cos x$
$250 = 117 + 205 - 2\sqrt{117}\sqrt{205}\cos x$
$x = \cos^{-1}\left(\dfrac{117 + 205 - 250}{2\sqrt{117 \times 205}}\right) = 76.6°$ (1 d.p.)

## The Return of the Cosine Rule — out now in 3D...

If you need to find an angle in a 3D question, don't panic — just put those standard trig formulas to work.

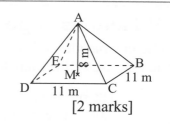

Q1 Find the size of the angle between the plane ACD and the plane BCDE in the square-based pyramid shown. M is the midpoint of its base. [2 marks]

# Trig Values

Trig questions quite often use the same angles — so it'll make life <u>easier</u> if you know the sin, cos and tan of these <u>commonly used</u> angles. You might need to use them in your non-calculator exam — so <u>learn</u> them.

## Use these Two Triangles to Learn the Trig Values

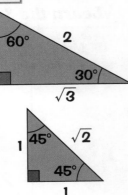

1)  You need to know the <u>values</u> of sin, cos and tan at **30°, 60°** and **45°**.

2)  To help you remember, you can <u>draw</u> these <u>two triangles</u>. It may seem a complicated way to learn a few numbers, but it <u>does</u> make it <u>easier</u>. Honest.

3)  If you draw the triangles, putting in their <u>angles</u> and <u>side lengths</u>, you can use them to work out the <u>special trig values</u> that you need to know.

4)  Use <u>SOH CAH TOA</u>...

$$\sin x = \frac{\text{opp}}{\text{hyp}} \qquad \cos x = \frac{\text{adj}}{\text{hyp}} \qquad \tan x = \frac{\text{opp}}{\text{adj}}$$

5)  ...to <u>learn</u> these <u>trig values</u>:

$$\sin 30° = \frac{1}{2} \qquad \sin 60° = \frac{\sqrt{3}}{2} \qquad \sin 45° = \frac{1}{\sqrt{2}}$$

$$\cos 30° = \frac{\sqrt{3}}{2} \qquad \cos 60° = \frac{1}{2} \qquad \cos 45° = \frac{1}{\sqrt{2}}$$

$$\tan 30° = \frac{1}{\sqrt{3}} \qquad \tan 60° = \sqrt{3} \qquad \tan 45° = 1$$

> You can use Pythagoras to check that you've got the side lengths right, e.g. $1^2 + (\sqrt{3})^2 = 4 = 2^2$

### EXAMPLES:

**1.** Without using a calculator, find the exact length of side $b$ in the right-angled triangle shown.

1)  It's a right-angled triangle so use SOH CAH TOA to pick the correct <u>trig formula</u> to use.
$$C = \frac{A}{H}$$

2)  Put in the <u>numbers</u> from the diagram in the question.
$$\cos 30° = \frac{b}{2}$$

3)  You know the <u>value</u> of <u>cos 30°</u>, so <u>substitute</u> this in.
$$\frac{\sqrt{3}}{2} = \frac{b}{2}$$
$$b = \sqrt{3}$$

**2.** This circle has radius 2 cm. Without using a calculator, find the exact area of segment A.

1)  Find the <u>area</u> of the <u>triangle</u> using the formula area $= \frac{1}{2}ab\sin C = \frac{1}{2}r^2\sin C$:

area of triangle $= \frac{1}{2} \times 2^2 \times \sin 45°$
$$= \frac{2}{\sqrt{2}} = \sqrt{2}$$

> For more on surds, see p14.

2)  Find the <u>area</u> of the <u>sector</u>:
$$\text{area of sector} = \frac{45}{360} \times \pi \times 2^2 = \frac{\pi}{2}$$

3)  Then <u>area</u> of <u>segment</u>
= area of sector − area of triangle:
$$\text{area of segment} = \frac{\pi}{2} - \sqrt{2} \text{ cm}^2$$

## Tri angles — go on, you might like them...

Use the triangles to learn the trig values — then if you're not sure about a trig value in the exam, you can quickly sketch the triangle to check you've got it right. Have a go at this Exam Practice Question.

Q1  The right-angled triangle shown has side lengths whose ratio $a:b:c$ is $1:\sqrt{3}:2$. What is the value of $x$?

[2 marks]

# Graphs of Trig Functions

Before you leave this page, you should be able to close your eyes and picture these three graphs in your head, <u>properly labelled</u> and everything. If you can't, you need to learn them more. I'm not kidding.

## *sin x* and *cos x* are always in the range –1 to 1

The graphs of <u>sin x</u> and <u>cos x</u> are similar — they just bob up and down between -1 and 1.

> sin x and cos x are both <u>periodic</u> (repeat themselves) with period 360°

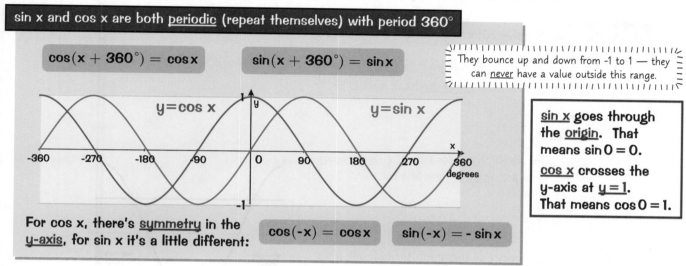

$$\cos(x + 360°) = \cos x \qquad \sin(x + 360°) = \sin x$$

*They bounce up and down from -1 to 1 — they can never have a value outside this range.*

<u>sin x</u> goes through the <u>origin</u>. That means sin 0 = 0.

<u>cos x</u> crosses the y-axis at <u>y = 1</u>. That means cos 0 = 1.

For cos x, there's <u>symmetry</u> in the <u>y-axis</u>, for sin x it's a little different:

$$\cos(-x) = \cos x \qquad \sin(-x) = -\sin x$$

## *tan x* can be Any Value at all

tan x is <u>different</u> from sin x or cos x — it goes between -∞ and +∞.

> Tan x is also periodic — but with period 180°

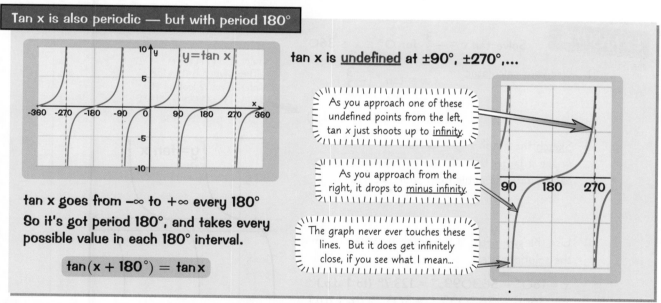

tan x is <u>undefined</u> at ±90°, ±270°,...

*As you approach one of these undefined points from the left, tan x just shoots up to <u>infinity</u>.*

*As you approach from the right, it drops to <u>minus infinity</u>.*

*The graph never ever touches these lines. But it does get infinitely close, if you see what I mean...*

tan x goes from –∞ to +∞ every 180°

So it's got period 180°, and takes every possible value in each 180° interval.

$$\tan(x + 180°) = \tan x$$

The easiest way to <u>sketch</u> any of these graphs is to plot the <u>important points</u> which happen every 90° (i.e. –180°, –90°, 0°, 90°, 180°, 270°, 360°...) and then just join the dots up.

---

## *Live a life of sin (and cos and tan)...*

It's really important that you can draw the graphs on this page and get all the labels right. You need to know where the graphs intersect the axes, and the maximum and minimum points of each graph.

Q1    Without using a calculator, which of the
      following is the correct graph of tan x?
      [1 mark]

# Solving Trig Equations in a Given Interval

Sometimes you'll be asked to <u>solve a trig equation</u> in a given <u>interval</u>. It's quite likely that there'll be <u>more than one</u> solution — the best way to go about these questions is to get the first solution using your calculator, then <u>sketch the graph</u> so you can find any other solutions.

## Sketch a Graph to find Solutions in an Interval...

**EXAMPLE:** Solve $\cos x = \frac{1}{2}$ for $0° \leq x \leq 360°$.

1) Get the first solution from your <u>calculator</u> — or in this case, you should <u>remember</u> that $\cos 60° = \frac{1}{2}$.

$$x = \cos^{-1} \frac{1}{2}$$
$$x = 60°$$

2) <u>Sketch</u> the graph of $y = \cos x$ for the <u>range</u> you're interested in and <u>mark on</u> the first solution.

3) Use the <u>symmetry</u> of the graph to work out what the <u>other</u> solution is:

$$x = 360° - 60° = 300°$$

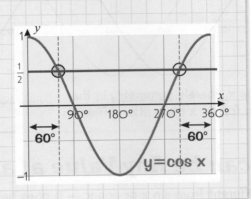

**EXAMPLE:** Solve $\tan x = -\frac{3}{2}$ for $0° \leq x \leq 360°$.

1) Use your <u>calculator</u>:

$$x = \tan^{-1}\left(-\frac{3}{2}\right)$$
$$x = -56.3099...°$$
$$x = -56.3° \text{ (to 1 d.p.)}$$

This solution isn't in the interval you're looking at.

2) <u>Sketch</u> the graph of $y = \tan x$.
Make it <u>larger</u> than the <u>range</u> you want, so you can include the <u>angle</u> from your calculator.

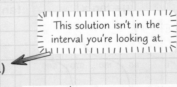

3) Use the <u>symmetry</u> of the graph to work out what the <u>solutions</u> are:

$$x = 180° - 56.3099...° = 123.7° \text{ (to 1 d.p.)}$$
$$x = 360° - 56.3099...° = 303.7° \text{ (to 1 d.p.)}$$

You should always use your graph to double check that you have the right number of solutions in the required interval.

## And I feel that love is dead, I'm loving angles instead...

Sketching the graph is a really useful way of seeing where the solutions are and how you're going to find them. Always check whether the answer given by your calculator is actually in the interval you want.

Q1     Solve $\sin x = 0.3$ in the interval $0° \leq x \leq 360°$.          [2 marks]

# Using Trig Identities

Now for something <u>really</u> exciting — trig identities.  Mmm, well, maybe exciting was the wrong word.

## *Look Out for Places to Use this Identity*

There's more on identities on p30.

$$\tan x \equiv \frac{\sin x}{\cos x}$$

This is a handy thing to know.  The most likely places to use it are:

1) Equations with a <u>sin</u> and <u>cos</u> where you can <u>divide</u> sin by cos, e.g. $5\sin x = \cos x$

2) Equations with a <u>tan</u>, together with a <u>sin</u> or a <u>cos</u>, e.g. $3\sin x - \tan x = 0$

 **EXAMPLE:**

Solve: $5\sin x = \cos x$, for $0° \le x \le 360°$.

1) It's got <u>sin</u> and <u>cos</u> in it — so divide through by cos $x$.

2) Now you can <u>substitute</u> in $\tan x = \frac{\sin x}{\cos x}$.

3) Use your <u>calculator</u> to find the <u>first</u> solution.

$$\frac{5\sin x}{\cos x} = 1 \implies 5\tan x = 1$$
$$\tan x = \frac{1}{5}$$
$$x = \tan^{-1}(0.2)$$
$$= 11.3099...$$

4) <u>Sketch</u> the graph of $y = \tan x$, then use it to work out the other <u>solutions</u>.

$$x = 180° + 11.3099...°$$
$$= 191.3099...°$$

So $x = 11.3°$, $191.3°$ (to 1 d.p.)

**EXAMPLE:**

Solve: $3\sin x - \tan x = 0$, for $0° \le x \le 360°$.

1) It's got <u>sin</u> and <u>tan</u> in it — so writing tan $x$ as $\frac{\sin x}{\cos x}$ is probably a <u>good</u> move:

2) <u>Multiply</u> the whole equation by <u>cos $x$</u>.

3) Now — there's a <u>common factor</u> of $\sin x$.

4) You've got two things <u>multiplying together</u> to make <u>zero</u> — so <u>either one or both</u> of them is equal to zero.

$$3\sin x - \tan x = 0$$
$$\implies 3\sin x - \frac{\sin x}{\cos x} = 0$$
$$\implies 3\sin x \cos x - \sin x = 0$$
$$\implies \sin x(3\cos x - 1) = 0$$
$$\implies \sin x = 0 \quad \text{or} \quad 3\cos x - 1 = 0$$

The first solution is... $x = \sin^{-1} 0 = 0°$

Now find the other points where sin $x = 0$ in the interval $0° \le x \le 360°$.

$$\implies x = 0°, 180°, 360°$$

Rearrange... $\cos x = \frac{1}{3} \implies x = \cos^{-1}\frac{1}{3}$

...then find the first solution.

$$= 70.5287...°$$
$$= 70.5° \text{ (to 1 d.p.)}$$

Sketch the graph of $y = \cos x$.

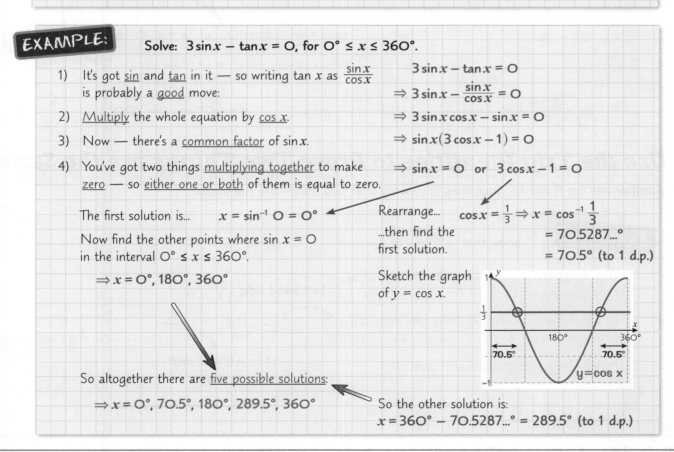

So altogether there are <u>five possible solutions</u>:

$$\implies x = 0°, 70.5°, 180°, 289.5°, 360°$$

So the other solution is:
$x = 360° - 70.5287...° = 289.5°$ (to 1 d.p.)

---

## *Trigonometry is the root of all evil...*

If you feel like you're getting stuck, rewriting stuff using different formulas is always worth trying.

Q1  Solve $7\tan x \cos x = 3$ in the interval $0° \le x \le 360°$.  [3 marks]

Q2  Solve $\tan x - \frac{3}{2}\sin x = 0$ in the interval $0° \le x \le 360°$.  [4 marks]

# Using Trig Identities

Another trig identity — and it's a good 'un.  You'll be given it in the exam, but you need to know how to use it.

## *If you have a sin² x or a cos² x, think of this Identity...*

$$\sin^2 x + \cos^2 x \equiv 1 \quad \Rightarrow \quad \begin{array}{l} \sin^2 x \equiv 1 - \cos^2 x \\ \cos^2 x \equiv 1 - \sin^2 x \end{array}$$

Be careful — $\sin^2 x$ means $(\sin x)^2$, <u>not</u> $\sin(x^2)$.

Use this identity to get rid of a sin² or a cos² that's making things awkward...

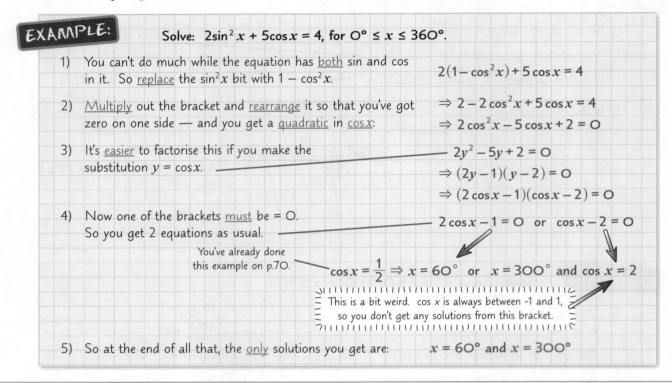

**EXAMPLE:**   Solve:  $2\sin^2 x + 5\cos x = 4$, for $0° \le x \le 360°$.

1) You can't do much while the equation has <u>both</u> sin and cos in it.  So <u>replace</u> the $\sin^2 x$ bit with $1 - \cos^2 x$.

$$2(1 - \cos^2 x) + 5\cos x = 4$$

2) <u>Multiply</u> out the bracket and <u>rearrange</u> it so that you've got zero on one side — and you get a <u>quadratic</u> in <u>cos x</u>:

$$\Rightarrow 2 - 2\cos^2 x + 5\cos x = 4$$
$$\Rightarrow 2\cos^2 x - 5\cos x + 2 = 0$$

3) It's <u>easier</u> to factorise this if you make the substitution $y = \cos x$.

$$2y^2 - 5y + 2 = 0$$
$$\Rightarrow (2y - 1)(y - 2) = 0$$
$$\Rightarrow (2\cos x - 1)(\cos x - 2) = 0$$

4) Now one of the brackets <u>must</u> be $= 0$. So you get 2 equations as usual.

You've already done this example on p.70.

$$2\cos x - 1 = 0 \quad \text{or} \quad \cos x - 2 = 0$$

$$\cos x = \frac{1}{2} \Rightarrow x = 60° \quad \text{or} \quad x = 300° \text{ and } \cos x = 2$$

This is a bit weird.  cos x is always between -1 and 1, so you don't get any solutions from this bracket.

5) So at the end of all that, the <u>only</u> solutions you get are:   $x = 60°$ and $x = 300°$

## *Use the Trig Identities to Prove Two Things are the Same*

Another use for these trig identities is proving that two things are the same.

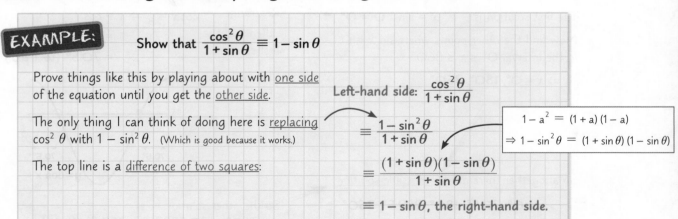

**EXAMPLE:**   Show that $\dfrac{\cos^2 \theta}{1 + \sin \theta} \equiv 1 - \sin \theta$

Prove things like this by playing about with <u>one side</u> of the equation until you get the <u>other side</u>.

The only thing I can think of doing here is <u>replacing</u> $\cos^2 \theta$ with $1 - \sin^2 \theta$.  (Which is good because it works.)

The top line is a <u>difference of two squares</u>:

Left-hand side: $\dfrac{\cos^2 \theta}{1 + \sin \theta}$

$$\equiv \frac{1 - \sin^2 \theta}{1 + \sin \theta}$$

$$1 - a^2 = (1 + a)(1 - a)$$
$$\Rightarrow 1 - \sin^2 \theta = (1 + \sin \theta)(1 - \sin \theta)$$

$$\equiv \frac{(1 + \sin \theta)(1 - \sin \theta)}{1 + \sin \theta}$$

$$\equiv 1 - \sin \theta, \text{ the right-hand side.}$$

## *Trig identities — the path to a brighter future...*

Those identities can be a bit daunting, but it's always worth having a few tricks in the back of your mind — look for things that factorise, or fractions that can be cancelled down, or ways to use those trig identities.

Q1     Show that $\cos \theta + 1 \equiv \dfrac{\sin^2 \theta}{1 - \cos \theta}$.                    [3 marks]

# Revision Questions for Section Five

There are a good few facts and formulas in this section, so use this page to check you've got them all sorted.

- Try these questions and <u>tick off each one</u> when you <u>get it right</u>.
- When you've done <u>all the questions</u> for a topic and are <u>completely happy</u> with it, tick off the topic.

## <u>2D Pythagoras and Trigonometry (p62-63)</u> ☑

1) A rectangle has a diagonal of 15 cm. Its short side is 4 cm.
   Calculate the length of the rectangle's long side to 1 d.p. ☑

2) Point C has coordinates (-1, 2) and point D has coordinates (4, -2).
   Calculate the length of the line CD to 1 d.p. ☑

3) Write down the three trigonometry formulas. ☑

4) Find the size of angle x in triangle ABC to 1 d.p. ☑

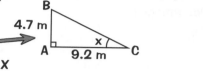

5) Find the length of side XY of triangle XYZ to 3 s.f. ☑

## <u>The Sine and Cosine Rules (p64-65)</u> ☑

6) Write down the sine and cosine rules and the formula (involving sin) for the area of any triangle. ☑

7) List the 4 different types of sine/cosine rule questions and which rule you need for each. ☑

8) Triangle ABC has side AB = 19 cm, side AC = 14 cm and angle ACB = 63°. Find angle ABC. ☑

9) Triangle PQR has side RQ = 3 km, PR = 23 km and angle PRQ = 10°. Find the length PQ. ☑

10) Triangle LMN has side LM = 6 m, side MN = 9.5 m and angle LMN = 54°. Find its area. ☑

## <u>3D Pythagoras and Trig (p66-67)</u> ☑

11) Find the length of the longest diagonal in the cuboid measuring 11 m × 18 m × 26 m. ☑

12) Find the angle between the line AG and the plane ABCD in this cuboid. ☑

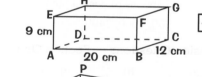

13) Find the size of angle TQV in the cuboid shown to the nearest degree. ☑

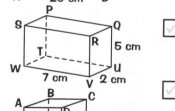

14) Find the acute angle between the planes BGE and EFGH in the cube shown. ☑

## <u>Trig Values, Graphs and Identities (p68-72)</u> ☑

15) Write down the exact value of tan 60°. ☑

16) Sketch the graphs for sin x, cos x and tan x for 0° ≤ x ≤ 360°,
    labelling all the max/min/zero/undefined points. ☑

17) Solve $\sin \theta = \dfrac{\sqrt{3}}{2}$ for 0° ≤ θ ≤ 360°. ☑

18) What is $\cos^2 x$ in terms of $\sin^2 x$? ☑

19) Prove that $1 + \tan^2 x = \dfrac{1}{\cos^2 x}$ ☑

20) Solve $3 \tan x + 2 \cos x = 0$ for −90° ≤ x ≤ 90°. ☑

21) Simplify: $(\sin y + \cos y)^2 + (\cos y - \sin y)^2$ ☑

22) Show that $\dfrac{\sin^4 x + \sin^2 x \cos^2 x}{\cos^2 x - 1} \equiv -1$ ☑

# Answers

## Section One

### Page 3 — Fractions
**Q1 a)** $\frac{39}{80}$ **b)** $\frac{2}{3}$

**c)** $\frac{139}{24} = 5\frac{19}{24}$ **d)** $-\frac{25}{12} = -2\frac{1}{12}$

**Q2** 50

### Page 4 — Fractions, Decimals and Percentages
**Q1 a)** $\frac{8}{10} = \frac{4}{5}$ **b)** $\frac{4}{100} = \frac{1}{25}$

**c)** $\frac{55}{100} = \frac{11}{20}$ **d)** $\frac{777}{1000}$

**e)** $\frac{64}{10} = \frac{32}{5}$

**Q2 a)** $\frac{5}{11}$ **b)** 63%

**Q3** $\frac{72}{999} = \frac{8}{111}$

### Page 5 — Percentages
**Q1** 806

**Q2** 34%

**Q3** 85% = £12 410,
so 1% = £146
and 100% = £14 600

### Page 7 — Ratios
**Q1 a)** 4:7 **b)** 2:3 **c)** 8:7

**Q2** 27 spoons of peanut butter

**Q3** 4200, 3000, 2400

### Revision Questions — Section One
**Q1 a)** $\frac{1}{3}$ **b)** $\frac{2}{3}$ **c)** $\frac{3}{5}$

**Q2 a)** $8\frac{3}{8}$ **b)** $\frac{58}{9}$

**Q3** Multiplying: Multiply top and bottom numbers separately.
Dividing: Turn the second fraction upside down, then multiply.
Adding/subtracting: Put fractions over a common denominator, then add/subtract the numerators.

**Q4 a)** $\frac{24}{55}$ **b)** $\frac{56}{15} = 3\frac{11}{15}$

**c)** $\frac{2}{15}$ **d)** $\frac{59}{8} = 7\frac{3}{8}$

**Q5** $\left(3\frac{3}{4} - 2\frac{1}{6}\right) \times 2\frac{2}{3} = \frac{19}{12} \times \frac{8}{3}$
$= \frac{38}{9} = 4\frac{2}{9}$

**Q6** 420 g

**Q7 a)** Divide the top by the bottom.
**b)** Put the digits after the decimal point on the top, and a power of 10 with the same number of zeros as there were decimal places on the bottom.

**Q8 a)** (i) $\frac{6}{100} = \frac{3}{50}$ (ii) 6%

**b)** (i) $\frac{35}{100} = \frac{7}{20}$ (ii) 0.35

**c)** (i) 0.55 (ii) 55%

**Q9** $0.\dot{5}\dot{4} = \frac{54}{99} = \frac{6}{11}$

**Q10 a)** 20 m **b)** £162 **c)** 62.5 km

**Q11** £33.60

**Q12** £4920

**Q13** 58.4%

**Q14** percentage change
= (change ÷ original) × 100

**Q15** 12.5%

**Q16** 21.84 ÷ 1.12 = 19.5 stone

**Q17 a)** 1:3 **b)** 2:3 **c)** 11:15

**Q18 a)** 2:3 **b)** 6:5 **c)** 5:3

**Q19** 1:6.25

**Q20** For every flute there are 2 violins. There are 5 flutes for every 2 trumpets, so there will be 10 violins for every 2 trumpets. As a ratio, this is 10:2 = 5:1.

**Q21** 180

**Q22** 114

**Q23** 1. Add up the parts
2. Divide to find one part
3. Multiply to find the amounts

**Q24** 750, 1000, 2250

## Section Two

### Page 9 — Powers and Roots
**Q1 a)** $p^4$ **b)** $18a^7b^2$
**c)** $27x^6y^9$ **d)** $4a^4b^5$

**Q2 a)** 8 **b)** $\frac{4}{5}$

**Q3** $u^6$

### Page 10 — Expanding Brackets
**Q1 a)** $y^2 + 2y - 24$
**b)** $2x^2 - 10x + 4xy^2$

**Q2 a)** $25p^2 - 40p + 16$
**b)** $9x^4 - 24x^2y + 16y^2$

### Page 11 — Expanding Brackets
**Q1 a)** $x^3 + 6x^2 + 3x - 10$
**b)** $a^3 + 15a^2 + 75a + 125$

### Page 12 — Factorising
**Q1** $3xy^2(3x + 5 + 4xyz^2)$

**Q2** $(2x + 1)(4x - 5)$

### Page 13 — Factorising
**Q1** $2(3a + b)(3a - b)$

**Q2** $(x^6 + 10y)(x^6 - 10y)$

**Q3** $\frac{7}{x + 8}$

**Q4** $(2 - x)(3x + 7)$

### Page 14 — Manipulating Surds
**Q1** $10 + 2\sqrt{5}$

**Q2** $4 - 2\sqrt{3}$

### Page 15 — Solving Equations
**Q1** $x = \pm 6$

**Q2** $x = 7$

### Page 17 — Rearranging Formulas
**Q1** $q = 4p + 12r$

**Q2** $z = \frac{y - 2x}{3}$

**Q3 a)** $y = \pm 3\sqrt{x}$ **b)** $y = \frac{xz}{2 - x}$

**Q4** $a = \frac{7 + 8b}{2b - 3}$

### Page 18 — Factorising Quadratics
**Q1** $(x + 3)(x - 7)$

**Q2** $x = 3$ or $x = 6$

### Page 19 — Factorising Quadratics
**Q1** $(2x + 3)(x - 5)$

**Q2** $x = \frac{2}{3}, x = -5$

**Q3** $(3x + 4)(x + 7)$

**Q4** $x = 3, x = -\frac{4}{5}$

### Page 20 — The Quadratic Formula
**Q1** $x = 0.23, x = -13.23$

**Q2** $x = \frac{3 + 3\sqrt{3}}{2}, x = \frac{3 - 3\sqrt{3}}{2}$

### Page 21 — Completing the Square
**Q1** $(x - 8)^2 - 53$
Note that p is negative here (it's −8) — so $(x + p)$ is actually $(x - 8)$.

**Q2** $(x + 4)^2 - 6 = 0$
$x = -4 + \sqrt{6}, x = -4 - \sqrt{6}$

### Page 22 — Completing the Square
**Q1 a)** $2(x + \frac{3}{4})^2 - \frac{49}{8}$
**b)** $x = 1, x = -\frac{5}{2}$

**c)** Minimum point = $(-\frac{3}{4}, -\frac{49}{8})$
Graph crosses the x-axis at
$x = 1, x = -\frac{5}{2}$

### Page 23 — Algebraic Fractions
**Q1** $\frac{x^2 + 2y}{x}$

**Q2** $\frac{6(x + 2)}{x^2(x + 5)}$

**Q3**  $\dfrac{5x+11}{(x-2)(x+5)}$

## Page 24 — Factorising Cubics

**Q1 a)**  f(3) = $3^3 - 5(3^2) - 2(3) + 24$
   $= 27 - 45 - 6 + 24 = 0$
   f(3) = 0, so $(x-3)$ is a factor
   of f(x).

**b)**  $(x-3)(x-4)(x+2)$

**c)**  $x = 3, x = 4, x = -2$

## Page 25 — Simultaneous Equations and Graphs

**Q1 a)**  $x = 3, y = 3$

**b)**  $x = 3, y = 4$ and $x = -4, y = -3$

## Page 26 — Simultaneous Equations

**Q1**  $x = -3, y = 3$

**Q2**  $x = 3, y = -1$

## Page 27 — Simultaneous Equations

**Q1**  $x = 0.5, y = -2.5$
   and $x = -4, y = 29$

**Q2**  $x = 4, y = -2$
   and $x = 10, y = 4$

## Page 28 — Inequalities

**Q1 a)**  $x < -7$    **b)**  $x \le -2.5$

## Page 29 — Inequalities

**Q1 a)**  $-7 < p < 7$

**b)**  $p \le -8$ or $p \ge 8$

**Q2**  $x = 0, 1, 2, 3, 4$

## Page 30 — Algebraic Proof

**Q1**  Take two consecutive odd
   numbers, $2n + 1$ and $2n + 3$,
   where $n$ is an integer.
   Then $(2n + 1) + (2n + 3) = 4n + 4$
   $= 2(2n + 2)$, which is even.

**Q2**  $(n + 6)^2 - n(n - 3)$
   $= n^2 + 12n + 36 - n^2 + 3n$
   $= 15n + 36 = 3(5n + 12)$,
   which is a multiple of 3.

## Page 31 — Sequences

**Q1**  5th term = –3, 16th term = 162,
   30th term = 722

**Q2 a)**  $4n + 1$    **b)**  33

## Page 32 — Sequences

**Q1**  $2n^2 - 2n + 6$

**Q2**  $\dfrac{1}{3}$

## Revision Questions — Section Two

**Q1 a)**  $x^3$    **b)**  $16x^{10}y^6$    **c)**  $20a^3b^6$

**Q2**  $x^{\frac{3}{4}} = 27$ means that $x = 27^{\frac{4}{3}}$
   $27^{\frac{4}{3}} = (\sqrt[3]{27})^4 = 3^4 = 81$, so $x = 81$

**Q3**  $x = 9^{\frac{3}{2}} = (\sqrt{9})^3 = 3^3 = 27$
   $y = \left(\dfrac{8}{125}\right)^{-\frac{1}{3}} = \sqrt[3]{\dfrac{125}{8}} = \dfrac{5}{2}$
   $xy = \dfrac{135}{2}$

---

**Q4 a)**  $12x^2 - 5x - 2$

**b)**  $6x^3 + 12x^2 - 3xy$

**c)**  $16x^2 - 8xy + y^2$

**Q5 a)**  $2x^2 + 3x^2y + 2xy^2 + 2xy - y^3$

**b)**  $4x^3 + 4x^2 - 7x + 2$

**Q6 a)**  $(p + q)(3p + 4q)$

**b)**  $(2x + 3y)(4x + 3y)$
   Factorise $8x^2 + 18x + 9$ first,
   then put in the y's.

**Q7 a)**  $5(a + 4b)(a - 4b)$

**b)**  $4(p^2 + 3q^5)(p^2 - 3q^5)$

**Q8**  $2\sqrt{3}$

**Q9**  $\dfrac{9 + 5\sqrt{3}}{6}$

**Q10 a)**  $x = 3.5$    **b)**  $x = \pm 5$

**Q11 a)**  $p = \dfrac{rq}{2 - r}$    **b)**  $p = \dfrac{2q - 7}{5}$

**Q12 a)**  $x = 4, x = -6$    **b)**  $x = 2, x = -\dfrac{4}{5}$

**Q13 a)**  $x = 1.70, x = -4.70$

**b)**  $x = 0.59, x = -5.09$

**c)**  $x = 0.91, x = -1.58$

**Q14 a)**  $x = 3 + \sqrt{7}, x = 3 - \sqrt{7}$

**b)**  $x = \dfrac{5}{2} + \dfrac{\sqrt{55}}{2}, x = \dfrac{5}{2} - \dfrac{\sqrt{55}}{2}$

**Q15**  $\dfrac{5x + 7}{(x - 1)(x + 3)}$

**Q16**  $(x + 2)(x + 7)(x - 3)$

**Q17**  $x = 1, y = -2$ or $x = -7, y = -18$

**Q18 a)**  $x \ge -3$    **b)**  $x < 13$

**Q19 a)**  $-5 \le x \le 5$    **b)**  $-3 < x < 9$

**Q20**  $(2n + 1)(2n - 1) = 4n^2 - 1$
   $= 2(2n^2) - 1$, which is odd for all
   integer values of $n$.

**Q21 a)**  $7n - 9$    **b)**  $n^2 - 2n + 3$

**Q22 a)**  First term = 0.455
   Eighth term = 0.224
   Fourteenth term = 0.214

**b)**  0.2

**Q23**  $\dfrac{1}{4}$

# Section Three

## Page 34 — Gradients

**Q1**  $-\dfrac{5}{2}$ or $-2.5$

## Page 35 — Equation of a Straight Line

**Q1 a)**  $y = \dfrac{1}{3}x - 4$    **b)**  $5x - 3y + 3 = 0$

## Page 36 — Drawing Straight-Line Graphs

**Q1**

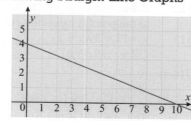

---

## Page 37 — Parallel and Perpendicular Lines

**Q1**  $y = x - 3$

**Q2**  Gradient of AB = –4

   Gradient of AC = $-\dfrac{3}{5}$

   Gradient of BC = $\dfrac{1}{4}$

   The lines AB and BC are
   perpendicular as their gradients
   multiply together to give –1
   $(-4 \times \dfrac{1}{4} = -1)$.
   So ABC is a right-angled triangle
   with a right angle at point B.

## Page 38 — Coordinates and Ratio

**Q1**  $(2, -2)$
   The centre of the circle is the
   midpoint of the line segment AB.

**Q2**  Use the information given to find
   the coordinates of P, Q and R:
   P = (–2, 0), Q = (0, 6), R = (4, 18)
   Then use the rule for the gradients
   of perpendicular lines to find the
   equation of the line:
   $18 = -\dfrac{1}{3} \times 4 + c \Rightarrow c = \dfrac{58}{3}$
   $y = -\dfrac{1}{3}x + \dfrac{58}{3}$ or $3y + x - 58 = 0$

## Page 39 — Functions

**Q1 a)**  $a = -2$    **b)**  $x \le -3$

## Page 40 — Functions

**Q1**  Lowest: f(1) = $a + b = 4$
   Highest: f(3) = $3a + b = 10$
   Solving simultaneously:
   $2a = 6 \Rightarrow a = 3, a + b = 4 \Rightarrow b = 1$

**Q2 a)**

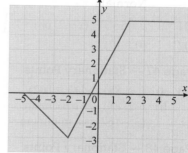

**b)**  $x = -12$
   f(x) ≤ 5 for x ≥ –2, so the solution
   of f(x) = 7 must be for x < –2.

## Page 41 — Quadratic Graphs

**Q1** **a)**

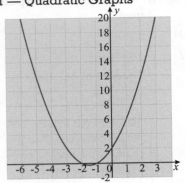

**b)** $x = -4.5$ (accept −4.3 to −4.7),
$x = 1.5$ (accept 1.3 to 1.7).

## Page 42 — Equation of a Circle

**Q1** **a)** $x^2 + y^2 = 36$
**b)** $(x + 4)^2 + (y - 3)^2 = 36$
The circle is translated 4 to the left and 3 up. So the new centre is (−4, 3), but the radius stays the same.

## Page 43 — Equation of a Circle

**Q1** $x^2 + y^2 = 34$ is the circle passing through (−5, 3)
$x^2 + y^2 - 2x + 4y + 4 = 0$ is the circle with centre (1, −2)
$x^2 + y^2 = 2(6x + 3y - 10)$ is the circle with radius 5

## Page 44 — Differentiation

**Q1** $3 + 6x^2$

**Q2** $9x^2 - 25x^4$

## Page 45 — Differentiation

**Q1** $2$

**Q2** $-312$

## Page 46 — Finding Tangents and Normals

**Q1** $y + 5 = -\dfrac{1}{4}(x + 2)$ <u>or</u> $y = -\dfrac{1}{4}x - \dfrac{11}{2}$

**Q2** $(0, -17)$

## Page 47 — Stationary Points

**Q1** **a)** $(-2, 88)$ and $(3, -162)$
**b)** $(-2, 88)$ is a maximum
$(3, -162)$ is a minimum

## Page 48 — Stationary Points

**Q1** **a)** $(0, 6)$

**b)** $\dfrac{dy}{dx} = -3x^2$

Point to the left: −0.5
$\dfrac{dy}{dx} = -0.75 < 0$

Point to the right: 0.5
$\dfrac{dy}{dx} = -0.75 < 0$

So the gradient is negative on both sides of the stationary point, therefore (0, 6) is a point of inflection.

## Page 49 — Curve Sketching

**Q1**

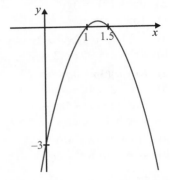

## Revision Questions — Section Three

**Q1** $2x + 2y = 5$

**Q2** Midpoint of PQ: $(1, 0)$
Gradient of PQ: $-\dfrac{1}{2}$
Perpendicular gradient: 2
Perpendicular bisector:
$y - 0 = 2(x - 1) \Rightarrow y = 2x - 2$

**Q3** OQ : QT = 1 : 2 $\Rightarrow$ Q = (5, 0)
SR : RT = 2 : 3 $\Rightarrow$ R = (6, −6)
Right-angled triangle with QR as hypotenuse has height 6, width 1.
Triangle POQ is similar to this triangle and has width 5, therefore height of POQ = 6 × 5 = 30 and P = (0, 30)
Instead, you could use points Q and R to find the equation of PQR, then use this to find the $y$-intercept P.

**Q4** **a)** −4
**b)** $x^2 \geq 0 \Rightarrow -x^2 \leq 0 \Rightarrow 5 - x^2 \leq 5$
So the range is f(x) ≤ 5
**c)** $5 - (2x)^2 = -95 \Rightarrow 4x^2 = 100$
$\Rightarrow x^2 = 25 \Rightarrow x = -5$ or $x = 5$

**Q5**

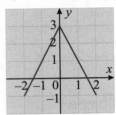

**Q6** $-1 \leq h(x) \leq 0$

**Q7** $x = -1.7$ (accept −1.8 to −1.6)
$x = 4.7$ (accept 4.6 to 4.8)

**Q8** $x^2 + y^2 = 64$

**Q9** Centre = (3, −7)　　　Radius = 9

**Q10** $35x^4 + 12x^2$

**Q11** $-13$

**Q12** A line perpendicular to the curve at the point it meets the curve.

**Q13** $y + 11 = 39(x + 2)$
<u>OR</u> $y = 39x + 67$

**Q14** **a)** $(0, -7)$

**b)** $\dfrac{dy}{dx} = 15x^2 > 0$ for $x \neq 0$
The gradient is positive except at $x = 0$, so (0, −7) is a point of inflection.

**Q15** **a)** Maximum at $\left(-\dfrac{2}{3}, 6\dfrac{5}{9}\right)$ and minimum at $\left(\dfrac{2}{3}, -\dfrac{5}{9}\right)$.

**b)**

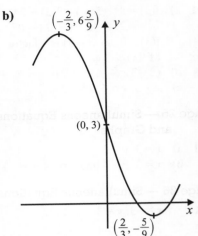

## Section Four

## Page 51 — Matrices

**Q1** $\begin{pmatrix} 9 \\ 2 \end{pmatrix}$

## Page 52 — Matrix Transformations

**Q1** $r = 4, s = 23$

## Page 53 — Matrix Transformations

**Q1** $\begin{pmatrix} -1 & 0 \\ 0 & 1 \end{pmatrix}$

**Q2**

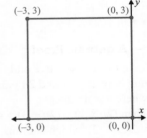

## Page 54 — Geometry

**Q1** $x = 67° + 67° = 134°$

## Page 55 — Geometry

**Q1** $x = 56°$

## Page 56 — Area

**Q1** **a)** 15.64 cm² **b)** 7.82 cm

## Page 57 — Surface Area and Volume

**Q1** $h = 2.5$ cm

## Page 58 — Volume

**Q1** $r = 8$ cm

## Page 60 — Circle Geometry

**Q1** Angle ABD = angle ACD = 52°
Using the alternate segment theorem gives you both of the required angles.

## Revision Questions — Section Four

**Q1** $\begin{pmatrix} -8 & -18 \\ -2 & 10 \end{pmatrix}$

**Q2** $\begin{pmatrix} 9 & 1 \\ -12 & 20 \end{pmatrix}$

**Q3** Reflection in the line $y = x$.

**Q4** Call the coordinates of L $(a, b)$.
$\begin{pmatrix} 1 & 4 \\ 2 & 2 \end{pmatrix}\begin{pmatrix} 3 & 3 \\ 0 & -3 \end{pmatrix}\begin{pmatrix} a \\ b \end{pmatrix} = \begin{pmatrix} 15 \\ 12 \end{pmatrix}$
$\begin{pmatrix} 3 & -9 \\ 6 & 0 \end{pmatrix}\begin{pmatrix} a \\ b \end{pmatrix} = \begin{pmatrix} 15 \\ 12 \end{pmatrix}$
$\begin{pmatrix} 3a - 9b \\ 6a \end{pmatrix} = \begin{pmatrix} 15 \\ 12 \end{pmatrix}$
$6a = 12 \Rightarrow a = 2$
$3a - 9b = 15 \Rightarrow 6 - 9b = 15$
$\Rightarrow b = -1$
Coordinates of L are $(2, -1)$.

**Q5** 360°

**Q6 a)** 106°
**b)** 142°
**c)** 65°

**Q7** 72°

**Q8** Circumference = $12\pi$ mm
Area = $36\pi$ mm²

**Q9** 17.45 cm

**Q10** $90\pi$ cm³

**Q11** 150.8 cm²

**Q12** 9 m

**Q13** 180°

**Q14** 24°

**Q15** Angle CEF = 46° (alternate angles),
therefore angle CDF = 46°
(angles in the same segment).
Angle EDF = 46°
(alternate segment theorem).
So angle CDE = 46° + 46° = 92°.

# Section Five

## Page 62 — Pythagoras' Theorem

**Q1** 7.6 m

**Q2** 24 m

**Q3** $\sqrt{61}$

## Page 63 — Trigonometry — Sin, Cos, Tan

**Q1** 3.27 m

## Page 64 — The Sine and Cosine Rules

**Q1** 38.6 cm²

## Page 65 — The Sine and Cosine Rules

**Q1** 29.6° (3 s.f.)

**Q2** 28.7 mm (3 s.f.)

## Page 66 — 3D Pythagoras

**Q1** 25.6 m (3 s.f.)

## Page 67 — 3D Trigonometry

**Q1** Make a right-angled triangle AMN, where N is the midpoint of DC. Then use $T = \dfrac{O}{A}$.
55.5° (3 s.f.)

## Page 68 — Trig Values

**Q1** 60°

## Page 69 — Graphs of Trig Functions

**Q1** B

## Page 70 — Solving Trig Equations in a Given Interval

**Q1** 17.5°, 162.5°

## Page 71 — Using Trig Identities

**Q1** 25.4°, 154.6° (3 s.f.)

**Q2** 0°, 48.2° (3 s.f.), 180°, 311.8° (3 s.f.), 360°

## Page 72 — Using Trig Identities

**Q1** $\dfrac{\sin^2\theta}{1 - \cos\theta} \equiv \dfrac{1 - \cos^2\theta}{1 - \cos\theta}$
$\equiv \dfrac{(1 - \cos\theta)(1 + \cos\theta)}{1 - \cos\theta}$
$\equiv 1 + \cos\theta$

## Revision Questions — Section Five

**Q1** 14.5 cm

**Q2** 6.4

**Q3** $S = \dfrac{O}{H}$  $C = \dfrac{A}{H}$  $T = \dfrac{O}{A}$

**Q4** 27.1°

**Q5** 6.74 cm

**Q6** See p.64.

**Q7** See p.65.

**Q8** 41.0° (3 s.f.)

**Q9** 20.1 km (3 s.f.)

**Q10** 23.1 m² (3 s.f.)

**Q11** 33.5 m (3 s.f.)

**Q12** 21.1° (3 s.f.)

**Q13** 57°

**Q14** 54.7° (3 s.f.)
If you're struggling to make a start on this question — try drawing the triangle BMF, where M is the midpoint of EG and FH.

**Q15** $\sqrt{3}$

**Q16**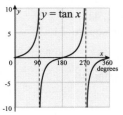

**Q17** 60°, 120°

**Q18** $\cos^2 x = 1 - \sin^2 x$

**Q19** $1 + \tan^2 x \equiv 1 + \dfrac{\sin^2 x}{\cos^2 x}$
$\equiv \dfrac{\cos^2 x + \sin^2 x}{\cos^2 x}$
$\equiv \dfrac{1}{\cos^2 x}$

**Q20** $3\tan x + 2\cos x = 0$
$3\dfrac{\sin x}{\cos x} + 2\cos x = 0$
$3\sin x + 2\cos^2 x = 0$
$3\sin x + 2(1 - \sin^2 x) = 0$
$2\sin^2 x - 3\sin x - 2 = 0$
$(2\sin x + 1)(\sin x - 2) = 0$
So $\sin x = -\dfrac{1}{2}$ or $\sin x = 2$
$\sin x = 2$ has no solutions
$x = \sin^{-1}\left(-\dfrac{1}{2}\right) = -30°$

**Q21** $(\sin y + \cos y)^2 + (\cos y - \sin y)^2$
$\equiv (\sin^2 y + 2\sin y \cos y + \cos^2 y) +$
$(\cos^2 y - 2\cos y \sin y + \sin^2 y)$
$\equiv 2(\sin^2 y + \cos^2 y) \equiv 2$

**Q22** $\dfrac{\sin^4 x + \sin^2 x \cos^2 x}{\cos^2 x - 1} \equiv -1$
LHS: $\dfrac{\sin^2 x(\sin^2 x + \cos^2 x)}{(1 - \sin^2 x) - 1}$
$\equiv \dfrac{\sin^2 x}{-\sin^2 x} \equiv -1 \equiv$ RHS

# Index